S0-ATB-763

African Lions and Cats

Other Books by B. F. BEEBE

American Bears
American Desert Animals
American Lions and Cats
American Wild Horses
American Wolves, Coyotes and Foxes
Appalachian Elk
Assateague Deer
Chestnut Cub
Coyote Come Home
Ocelot
Run, Light Buck, Run
Yucatan Monkey
Animals South of the Border
African Elephants

African Lions And Cats

by
B. F. Beebe

Illustrated by James Ralph Johnson

DAVID McKAY COMPANY, INC.
NEW YORK
1969

African Lions and Cats
COPYRIGHT © 1969 BY
B. F. Beebe

All rights reserved, including the right to reproduce
this book, or parts thereof, in any form, except for
the inclusion of brief quotations in a review.

LIBRARY OF CONGRESS CATALOG CARD NUMBER: 69–12950
MANUFACTURED IN THE UNITED STATES OF AMERICA

To Yump Johnson, *Safari Companion*
Waltham, Massachusetts

CHAPTERS

African Lions and Cats

1: *Cheetahs*

PERHAPS THE MOST UNIVERSALLY ACCEPTED FALLACY
about African animals is that the cheetah is the fastest. It is not. The cheetah is fast, having been roughly
clocked by vehicle at close to seventy miles an hour.
It can outrun most antelopes and is over twice as fast
as the best human sprinter.

However, it cannot run faster than a lion. Traditionally the African lion has been put in the fifty-mile-
an-hour class. Alan Tarlton, who has lived and filmed
in East Africa most of his adult life, reported some
specific data to *Africana* magazine in 1964.

He explained that during a 1937 film safari he and
his party saw a male lion, already gorged on a kill,
jump up in pursuit of a cheetah going "full belt" after
a Grant's gazelle. The cheetah had forty yards' start
on the lion but the lion overtook the cheetah within
100 yards and broke its back.

After stopping the cheetah's suffering with a pistol
shot Tarlton and his companions measured the distances involved. Fortunately, the entire event had been
recorded on film.

Perhaps the most accurate records of cheetah speed

were obtained in 1937 by Raymond Hook, who had trained African cheetahs to hunt. Hook took cheetahs to England and made his recordings at a greyhound race track. An electrical timing device was used, activated when the cheetahs broke light beams, a method considerably more accurate than timing over rough ground with an automobile speedometer. It recorded a cheetah speed of slightly over sixty miles an hour.

One factor accounting for the cheetah's highly-respected speed is its relatively slow heartbeat. As speed increases during a run the pulse can increase as necessary. Athletes develop slower pulse rates for this reason. Such similar animals as the rabbit and hare have significantly different running capacities because of different pulse rates. A rabbit with a pulse of 200 cannot run the distances achieved by the hare which has a pulse rate of seventy or below. However, the cheetah is not able to match the explosive energy which the lion musters for a sudden charge.

A friend of Tarlton's filmed a lioness making her final rush at a puku cob antelope. The lioness was coming down a slight slope and the cameraman recorded her charge with a 16 mm movie camera with a specific number of frames per second. With this data, plus measured ground distances, the cameraman was able to calculate her speed at about 100 miles an hour.

Alexander Lake, who hunted a lifetime in Africa as a safari guide and market hunter took many parties out after lions. He timed lions covering 100 yards from a standing start in four seconds. Lake reported that Martin Johnson claimed a lion could do this in three seconds or well over sixty miles an hour from a standing start.

Apparently the lion is incapable of such speed under normal circumstances. The phenomenon has been described as a short, explosive charge by Frank W. Lane, an experienced student of lion behavior. He believed that the sudden physical change which takes place in a lion's body when it launches a blistering charge resembles an explosion more than it does a bodily function. The lion's large adrenal glands flood the blood with sudden discharges of vitalizing sugar, a "crisis-energy producing secretion," in Lane's words and immediately the lion's nerves, lungs and brain shift into high gear as does the heart which is nearly as big as a man's head. The animal's astonishing strength is compressed into an energy outburst which lasts only a few seconds. During such a moment the lion in effect becomes a super lion. The phenomenon is not exclusive. A diminutive housewife could never be expected to lift a car, yet when her child is caught beneath an automobile wheel, more than one mother has been known to lift the vehicle off her child.

Once an angered lion begins such a charge it takes more than the destruction of a vital organ to stop it. Many lion hunters, quite literally many, have been mauled or killed after a heavy caliber bullet smashed the heart. One hunter put a bullet through a lion's heart at twenty yards but was knocked down by the lion which reared on its hind legs and died on top of him.

Why have these facts not been generally known before to naturalists? It is due to the relative ease of clocking the plains-loving cheetah whose flight has often been followed by safari or game-viewing vehicles. The lion is not an animal easily chased across flat ground since such terrain is not its common habitat. It prefers the brush and shade of rolling or rough ground. When disturbed it usually slips aside into cover rather than compete with a vehicle.

Lions have an almost instinctive hatred for cheetahs. The lion views the cheetah as a competitor poaching on its private preserve and will likely stop any activity, stalking, eating or sleeping, to go after a cheetah. That the latter's cubs may be killed frequently by lions is suggested by observations of lions taking or attempting to take cheetah cubs.

One such observation was made recently in Nairobi National Park by N. G. Hardy. A cheetah and four small cubs wandered near a dry wash, or donga, which a lioness considered her territory. One cub moved too close to the donga and the lioness began a stalk. Each time she charged the cheetah mother diverted her by running across her front. Hardy quickly notified the head ranger and the two sped out in a Landrover to drive between lioness and cheetah and stop the attacks.

Another Nairobi National Park lion recently killed an aging male cheetah and ate part of it. In South Africa's Kruger National Park a photographer recorded an attack on a pregnant female cheetah by two lionesses. The two mauled her so badly before she got away that it was apparent she could not survive the wounds.

A similar incident was described by Desmond Varaday in his *Gara-Yaka, The Story of a Cheetah*. Varaday, a game warden on a private reserve in the Bechuanaland Protectorate, was following his tame cheetah into the brush. She was about to give birth to cubs and Varaday wanted to be on hand in case she needed help. Soon after she stepped into the brush he saw her ears lift and it was obvious to him that something was agitating her.

Two lionesses pushed into sight. She tried to turn back to Varaday but the lionesses cut her off. Varaday was not armed and before he could devise some way of helping her the lionesses were on her, attacking from either side as she tried to defend herself, slashing furiously with her only cat-like claws, the dew claws inside her legs. She tried to run to Varaday but they cut her off once more.

He threw his hat at them, followed by stones, but they continued their mauling of the cheetah. Varaday and a friend then seized a dead thorn bush and rushed the lionesses, finally sending them loping away. The bleeding cheetah was hurried to Varaday's own bed where she gave birth to three cubs a few moments later. She and two of her cubs survived.

Fortunately for the cheetah it seldom comes into close contact with the lion because it tends to remain away from the scattered brush favored by lions. Its prey is usually found on the open plains.

Although most prey animals taken by Africa's cats are healthy adult animals enough observations of predator attacks against unhealthy prey have been made to suggest that the following situation is common. A cheetah will walk close to a herd of antelope grazing casually but watching it. The cheetah lies down in full view and studies the herd.

Game biologist Richard Estes found that Grant's gazelles on the plains of Ngorongoro's crater floor drew an imaginary line between themselves and a cheetah about seventy yards out. If the cheetah crossed that line they moved away, aware that this distance was sufficent to prevent a cheetah's sprinting all out from overtaking them. Consequently, they grazed quietly and kept the cheetah under surveillance. Like the other cats the cheetah must surprise if he is to be successful in taking prey. He must get close enough for his sprint to be successful before showing himself.

But suddenly the gazelles or antelopes become aware of the cheetah beginning a stalk. Heads come up; they seem to sense the cheetah's object. As the cheetah breaks into a charge the herd splits apart to allow the cheetah to dash past. The single prey animal dashes from the herd and away from the cheetah. For some reason it does not feel compelled to go all out and the cheetah quickly downs it.

Now the cheetah whistles its cubs or companions in to the kill. They walk through the herd without causing alarm. The antelope watch or continue grazing. Some naturalists who have watched such hunts are convinced that the prey animal senses its time has come and knows it has no chance to escape. On other occasions individual animal personalities assert themselves and one gazelle may fight valiantly while its companions flee. The wildebeest often fights back and at different times has put to flight all the cats including lions. Occasionally domestic goats tied as bait animals near hunters have butted charging lions with sufficient fury to send the lion fleeing.

The hyenas of Tanzania's Ngorongoro Crater have given naturalists the best opportunity to study selection of unhealthy prey. There the high population of hyenas causes them to become true predators, taking live animals rather than waiting for carrion or scraps. A hyena will rush at a wildebeest herd to make it split. Each wildebeest runs a few steps and this gives the hyena enough time to glimpse a limping animal or laggard calf. If it does see one, it begins pursuit. If it does not, it wanders away.

The cheetah is well aware of its speed limitations. Probably most initial pursuits are made at about forty-five miles an hour, a speed achieved in a few bounds.

If the selected healthy antelope heads straight out the cheetah usually gives up the chase. If it breaks aside the cheetah turns on real speed. This killing rush usually overtakes prey within 100 yards. If it does not, the the cheetah gives up the chase since its staying power is not equal to the antelope's.

When the cheetah reaches the prey it slaps the hindquarters to knock it down, then it seizes the throat. The experienced cheetah quickly places itself along the prey's back to avoid flailing hoofs until the prey suffocates. When chasing small prey such as the African hare the cheetah throws out a front leg and snags the hare as it breaks to one side. This is done without breaking its own stride.

The cheetah's feet are ideal for racing across Africa's plains. Since the claws are not entirely retractile they cannot be withdrawn into sheaths like those of other cats, but remain exposed the same as canines to allow good purchase, or digging into, the soil. The pads of an adult cheetah are hard like those of a dog and it can rush recklessly over sharp pebbles and stubble without the discomfort which other cats would suffer.

Although it would seem that the cheetah's keen eyesight would diminish the quality of other senses this does not appear to be the case. Varaday noticed that cheetah cubs could hear beetles crawling nearby and their sense of smell seemed as keen as any predator. They often became agitated or restless when distant animals moved past unseen.

The cheetah is occasionally forced to hunt by scent rather than sight in some of its habitat, especially in areas of high grass or brush which conceal prey. Most of the time its nostrils are sifting the breeze for an air trail, scent left in the air by an animal's passing, or moved by a breeze, or a brush trail which is the scent left on grass or brush after an animal has touched it in passing. Frequently, it will follow a track like a persistent hound, sniffing the scent left by animal feet. So effective is the cheetah's ability as a trail animal that it can lope along like a hound and dip its nose occasionally to confirm the trail.

After an exhausting chase the cheetah pants with outstretched tongue in the manner of a dog. Saliva drips freely from the mouth during this period of breath-getting.

All cats with long tails use them as balancing poles but the slim-bodied cheetah may have the most effective one among the big cats. During a sprint the tail whips around in a small circle to assist balance and when it is necessary to flip aside after dodging prey the long tail acts as a rudder to allow the cheetah to change direction without breaking stride.

Game biologist Richard Estes has pointed out that the cats' anatomies are the most specialized of all the carnivores for a particular technique of predation. These include the long, lithe body with powerful, quick muscles, relatively short limbs with retractable claws (except in the cheetah), front-facing eyes with powerful binocular vision, and long canine teeth for gripping and killing prey. Cats direct their attack at the prey's throat or neck while canines attack larger animals from the rear.

Oddly, the cheetah's chief physical characteristics parallel those of the canines: a deep, narrow chest, longer legs, and claws which are only partially retractable. However, the cheetah's final closure with its prey is typically cat-like rather than dog-like.

Unlike most cats the cheetah hunts by day or night as its needs require. However, Desmond Varaday, who had free-running cheetahs in his camp for years, found that his would not hunt at night. They spent the night resting and waited until dawn to begin their hunts.

A recent survey of 173 cheetah kills showed gazelles and impala accounting for almost sixty percent of the twenty-five species of animals and birds taken. The gazelles, Thomson's and Grant's gazelles, were by far the most popular prey. Larger hoofed animals such as zebras were seldom taken but the yearlings or younger of zebras, wildebeest, hartebeest, waterbuck and oryx apparently were taken whenever the opportunity offered.

Ostriches, guinea fowls, greater bustards, jackals, wart hogs and hares were among those recorded. Small animals and birds may play a larger part in the cheetah's diet than suspected since these can be caught unobtrusively and eaten quickly. Africa's fauna is far richer than America's in game birds the size of ducks

Cheetah

or larger that spend most of their time on the ground. These include helmeted guinea fowl, vulturine guinea fowl, crested guinea fowl, red-necked spur fowl, eight species of francolins, black-bellied bustard, white-bellied bustard and the larger Kori bustard, secretary bird and ground hornbill. The cheetah stalks them much like a housecat stalking a bluebird, attempting to get close enough before being seen so the leap can be successful. The cheetah is so fast that it often catches the birds before they can leave the ground, but if they do, the cheetah seldom misses snatching them out of the air with forefeet.

When more than one cheetah hunt together their hunt is a coordinated, preplanned effort. One cheetah moves across upwind to flush the birds while another moves downwind and into position to snatch one.

Do animals think and plan activities in which they control the action at a future time? Yes, they do. It appears that gregarious predators plan hunts as carefully as human predators.

Just how different an animal's thinking capacity is has been a matter of much conjecture and the outcries of anthropomorphism, or humanizing, raised so indignantly and fashionably by zoologists against animal writers of a few years ago, have slowed. A few years ago no self-respecting zoologist was willing to admit that an animal had enough mental capacity to reason and solve problems of consequence. Certainly no true scientist would accept the observation of an "untrained" native of the wilderness, African or American, who had seen animals perform surprising tasks over and over again. The scientist, jealous of his academic shaping of viewpoint, believed he was objective about all observations. He was a behaviorist, purely and simply. Animals behaved according to the patterns laid out in the genes of their species, like computers programed with specific tapes. Anyone who suggested that animals had strong personalities of their own and at times violated species behavior right and left was amusing, if not naive. Certainly a native African who claimed that he had watched Egyptian vultures use rocks as tools to break ostrich eggs was thought to be repeating a myth.

Then an occasional naturalist saw examples of tool-using and reasoning in wildlife and took movies of the event. Grudgingly, the behaviorist had to tighten his definition of anthropomorphism. Animals did share with human beings certain mental capacities.

We like to think that we are so mentally superior to all animals that they cannot grasp mathematics. Perhaps no animal, not even an ape, can count or share any of our use of mathematics. However, the more we learn about animals the more we discover what they have learned already.

The cheetah is a more fastidious feeder than the lion and leopard. It does not eat carrion, nor does it eat animals with fat. It likes lean meat only and the fur and feathers ingested while eating comprise only incidental roughage. The cheetah eats almost all of birds and small animals in order to get the liver and other organs for which its dietary needs create an appetite.

The cheetah, *Acinonyx jubatus raineyi* to the zoologist, is sometimes called the hunting leopard because it is frequently seen out in the open stalking game. It is about the length of the leopard but much thinner and with long legs. Because it cannot retract its claws fully it is not recognized as a true cat and the zoologist finds numerous differences between it and the leopard. The cheetah has an almost gentle expression compared to the cold threat which seems always to be on the leopard's face. Cheetah spots are small round black spots compared to the leopard's rosettes. The cheetah almost has a mane on the back of its neck as well as a cheek ruff. The leopard has neither. The cheetah's canine teeth are inferior to those of the leopard and in a fight the cheetah would stand little chance against the leopard. Its jaw is weaker and head is smaller.

The cheetah reaches adult weights of ninety to 135 pounds, about ten pounds less than the leopard.

In distant grass the cheetah's spots are difficult to distinguish and its tawny overtones may cause it to be mistaken for a lion. The spots at any distance, however, have an amazing capacity to help the cheetah's silhouette melt into almost any background in its habitat. It is easy enough to pass a resting cheetah a few yards away without seeing it. The cheetah does not hesitate to stroll across a burned flat plain and will settle down a quarter mile or more from the slightest cover in complete confidence that its wonderful camouflage and speed will provide adequate security.

All cheetahs are not spotted in the strict sense. The King, or striped, cheetah is a mutation of the ordinary species occurring in southern Rhodesia and northern South Africa. It has been assigned the name *Acinonyx rex*. Its pelage has few round spots but many splotches and irregular spots, especially toward the hindquarters. The splotches on the upper surface of its tail form an almost solid stripe down its length.

Strangely, a black cheetah seems never to have been observed. The other spotted African cats, leopards, genets and servals, are not especially rare in the melanistic, or black coloring, but so far a black cheetah apparently has not appeared.

The cheetah has none of the leopard's belligerence. It is timid, even shy, and is rarely aggressive even when cornered or trapped. Because of its mild disposition it is a popular pet and is almost as affectionate as a dog. Desmond Varaday, raising an orphaned female cub in southern Africa, put the cub against his feet at night. After she was grown and had her own cubs she still enjoyed sleeping on his bed at every opportunity. When she was a cub she considered Varaday her mother and whenever she found him relaxing she would hop into his lap. When he was napping on his bed during the day she settled onto his chest, purring, rubbing her face against his cheek and staring into his eyes. An amazing confidence was accorded Varaday by this cheetah. When she took her own cubs out to hunt she communicated to them exactly what tactics she expected of them. If Varaday did not cooperate in the project like a second adult cheetah she let him know her displeasure by having nothing to do with him for several days.

Although retiring, the cheetah is by no means a coward. Varaday may have witnessed one of Africa's rarest scenes. He saw his pet cheetah attack a leopard weighing 130 pounds, significantly larger than the cheetah.

The cheetah was lying by his campfire one evening in company with several dogs. Suddenly the leopard burst from the brush and seized a dog which the cheetah considered a favorite companion. As the leopard headed back into the brush with the screaming dog in its mouth the cheetah leaped upon the leopard's back, fixed its teeth in the back of the leopard's neck and shook it hard enough to force it to drop the dog.

The leopard threw itself down and dislodged the cheetah. Then it jumped atop the cheetah. The cheetah lashed up with hind legs, raking the leopard's underside severely and preventing it from getting a death grip. By this time Varaday and his helpers rushed the leopard, hurling burning limbs and shouting. The effect was enough to send the leopard fleeing. A few days later Varaday shot the leopard when it charged him during a bird-banding mission. Its skin measured eight feet and one inch, the biggest leopard he had ever seen.

Months later when his pet had two half-grown cubs of her own Varaday watched from a distance as a leopard with its newly-killed antelope climbed into a tree near the cubs and mother who were resting with the returned father cheetah. The inexperienced cubs began "stalking" the leopard. One even pulled himself up the tree trunk until the leopard's coarse cough stopped it.

The cub jumped down and joined his sister in yapping at the leopard which snarled and coughed in return. The two adult cheetahs rushed over and herded their youngsters to a safer spot. The leopard decided to find a tree away from the watching cheetahs but as soon as it brought its prey down, the cheetahs rushed it and the leopard hurried back into the same tree.

It was apparent to the watching Varaday that the leopard was furious about this affront. The cheetahs seemed well aware of its rising temper and turned to leave, but before they did, the father cheetah marked the tree as his territory by squirting it with urine from ten feet away. Then the four walked away.

More surprising still was the behavior of one cheetah toward a lioness. An observer watching a cheetah charge an impala herd saw the cheetah's selected target go down unexpectedly before the attack of a lioness whose presence had been unsuspected by the cheetah. Both cats stopped in surprise. The lioness sank to her heels ready to leap at the intruder.

The cheetah did the same, hissed, then leaped to the lion to slap her ear, followed by a cuff to her face. Before the lioness could react the cheetah whirled and sprinted away.

2: The Cheetah's Family Life

CHEETAH CUBS ARE BORN BLIND AFTER A GESTATION period of only ninety-three days and are helpless for the first week or ten days until their eyes open. They are hairless when first born and generally remain spotless for a time. The tops of heads and back are soon covered with long, soft gray hair, a protection against sun and rain during the early weeks.

Underparts are black initially because the black hair growing from the areas which will later reveal themselves as almost round spots is significantly longer than the white hair. After a few weeks white and black hair reaches equal lengths and the spotted pelage is now clearly defined. The long, gray hair or "mane" on back and head remains for some time before it is shed.

The cheetah mother spends almost all of the time when she is with her cubs licking and cleaning them. In contrast to the downy silken feel of a housekitten's belly fur, that beneath the cheetah cub's body is coarse, sparse and long. The reason for this rough pelage seems to be the need for quick evaporation of urine which cheetah cubs dribble almost every hour of the day. The cheetah mother spends much time drying these damp little bellies.

Like dogs cheetahs enjoy dust baths. Since the sparseness of their pelages is about the same, it is no great problem for either to shake off the dust. The dust bath serves several purposes. The most pleasurable is the sensation of dust against the skin, like water at a swimming hole to a boy or girl. The practical result, however, is to discourage external parasites such as bush-ticks and fleas, both of which can build serious infestations in the animal's pelage.

There is much to learn about the cheetah's family life in the wild. Game warden Varaday found three cheetah cubs two days after their mother had been killed by a crocodile. He estimated them to be two weeks old, much too young to be deprived of their mother's milk. The family life apparently parallels that of coyote cubs that survive the mother's death because of the father coyote's devotion to the family. Varaday found that the father cheetah, during the two days since the mother had been dead, had been disgorging food for the cubs but they were too young to touch it. Later when his pet had cubs of her own he found that the mother began regurgitating food when the cubs were two months old. They ate this voraciously and never seemed satisfied. The initial six meals a day were gradually reduced to three.

Before long the cubs let Varaday know that he was

Cheetah with month-old cubs

expected to share some of the food whenever he was eating and they only ate his chewed offerings. Later the step to fresh raw meat was abrupt. When he secured a dead francolin fowl dropped by a fleeing jackal and gave this to the cubs they immediately began a furious, growling tug-of-war which tore the bird apart. They ate most of the feathers, the bones and the meat, leaving only the wing and tail feathers.

Robert Cade, Superintendent of Nairobi National Park's Animal Orphanage, believes that the cheetah mother normally does not bring food to her cubs. The cheetah mother downs her prey, then calls her cubs to it.

The call is often mistaken for that of a bird. The cub's call is almost identical to the adult's but slightly higher. The sound is a chirp, even close to a whistle and precedes other cheetah sounds. A chirp followed by a hiss is a threat. A chirp and purring indicate satisfaction and a chirp and growl show anger or surprise, all sounds easily recognized by anyone who has been associated with a cheetah.

It is probably during later hunting periods, while cubs are coming from cover to the new kill, that most cubs are snatched up by predators such as jackals, birds of prey, hyenas, or lions.

I watched a cheetah mother and her two cubs one month old amble across a barren stretch of the Serengeti Plains. The cubs were too young to run and the mother forced herself to walk slowly so that neither

was more than a few steps away even when our vehicle was close enough to concern her. We took care
not to approach too close and agitate her and she
obliged us by settling to the ground. Here she lay
with head raised in a studied stare past us while her
cubs gathered behind her shoulders. After our photography was finished we eased away.

Later at the Seronera ranger headquarters veteran
game ranger Ken Scott told us that this cheetah had
given birth to six healthy cubs a month before but
four had been taken by hyenas while the mother was
away hunting.

When Varaday found his orphaned cheetah cubs he
saw they were badly in need of milk. Fortunately he
had his dog along at the time, a fox terrier with two
unweaned pups. Varaday laid her down and set the
cheetah cubs at her stomach. The fox terrier mother
had little sympathy for these clawing little strangers
pulling at her and snarled. Varaday calmed her and
she allowed the hungry little cubs to fill themselves.
However, as soon as Varaday got them home the dog
would have little to do with them and he had to
switch to powdered milk.

Varaday soon found the cubs afflicted with running
digestive systems. To stop this he mixed charcoal
dust and a pinch of bismuth with their milk. This
worked only temporarily and he finally had to resort
to a stronger, ill-tasting medicine which caused no
little trouble in feeding. The largest cub, a female,

had a healthy start over her two litter mates and developed rapidly while the other two weakened.

One incident that soon followed emphasized the dog-like characteristics of the cheetah and pointed out its inability to act like a cat. One of the litter mates lunged from the hands of a standing man in an attempt to get to a bottle. It fell heavily on its side instead of its feet, a fall so severe that it died from the internal injuries received.

One man who reared a cheetah cub in a household containing pups of about the same age said that the young cheetah made itself practically a member of the dog family. It apparently considered itself a dog and behaved like one, learning to do everything the dog did except bark.

During play with the pups the cheetah cub usually stalked the pups, charging unexpectedly at them and bowling them over. Occasionally a pup would surprise the cheetah and this apparently scared it momentarily. The cheetah assumed more cat-like characteristics then, arching its back and leaping sidewise as it slapped the pup while spitting vigorously.

Cheetahs do appear to get along with dogs better than other African cat family members. Dogs seem less inclined to classify the cheetah as a cat as far as their instinctive prejudices are concerned. Robert Cade has raised tiny cheetah cubs by placing them among a litter of puppies. The mother seemed as pleased with them as her pups, although Cade had to trim cheetah claws periodically to make certain that they did not wear out their welcome while nursing.

Unlike dogs, however, cheetahs appear to have no love for water, perhaps because of their usual open-country habitat. When it rains there are rarely any shelters available for protection and they are soaked. They spend some cold miserable hours until they are dry. In contrast lions and leopards have frequently been seen to wade and swim freely.

Because the average cheetah lives almost a solitary life instead of in cooperating prides the chances of survival to adulthood for cheetah cubs are less than those for lion cubs. If the cheetah mother is killed while the cubs are still dependent upon her they will probably starve. There are no foster mothers to adopt them as there are in a lion pride.

Superintendent Cade told of three "well-grown" cheetah cubs wandering into a Kenya township. They were thinner than he believed possible for living cheetahs. Two died shortly but one survived after much care. Cade believed the three had drifted about for days, gradually starving, after an accident to their mother.

A characteristic of cheetah cub foot pads is their unusual sensitiveness until they are about half a year old. The early pads are so tender that whenever a young cub steps on a sharp grass stalk or twig it squeaks in pain.

Young cheetahs develop faster than lions and seem

to have more intellectual skill when it comes to stalking and taking prey. They lose quickly the roly-poly awkwardness common to lion cubs and rapidly develop the long, lithe legs and body characteristic of their kind.

As might be expected cheetah cubs in the same litter show quite different personalities. One owner of a pet cheetah with two cubs said the female was a shy, affectionate and almost lazy cub while the male showed opposite inclinations of alertness, roughness and aggressiveness.

A cheetah's affection is gratifying to those who deserve it. By this I mean the person who raises a cheetah in its natural habitat, not the person who forces a leashed cheetah to stalk along Fifth Avenue to gratify a craving for distinction. Desmond Varaday allowed his pet cheetah complete freedom to come and go. After the cheetah's own cubs were born and reared principally in the brush she periodically returned to Varaday's camp. Once after weeks of separation she walked out of the night, licked the napping man's hand and jumped into his lap, bowling him over and giving him an unforgettable fright. That night she crawled into his camp cot and occasionally stretched her legs against his back, almost pushing him off.

Although there are always exceptions to any pattern of behavior, the cheetah's mild manner seems to be the only factor which encourages man to keep him as a "pet." East African game men who have had the longest association with the cheetah in the wild and in captivity are convinced that the average cheetah only tolerates humans and is interested only in things which have a real relationship to cheetahs. Many pet owners believe that the same viewpoint is held by all members of the cat family, including most housecats of whatever breed, in strong contrast to canines.

Because of their speed and tractability cheetahs have been used for centuries as hunters, chiefly in India. After Indian cheetahs became unavailable in the early 1900's, some Indian maharajahs periodically sent agents to East Africa to purchase adult cheetahs for training as hunters. The hunting methods were similar to those used by falconers. The cheetah chased the prey and killed it for the owner. The Moghul Emperor Akbbar who died in 1605 kept a thousand cheetahs for this purpose.

Apparently the last Indian cheetahs were killed in 1947 when a hunter shot three males by spotlighting them at night. However, Indian wildlife students believe the underlying cause of their cheetahs' extinction was the removal of their prey—black buck, gazelles and chitals—by overhunting, as well as the encroachment of farming and grazing.

For all practical purposes trying to exercise a captive cheetah on a leash and keep it in proper condition is like trying to keep a greyhound in a box without severe muscle atrophy and deteriorating health. A cheetah can only be exercised properly in a large area of many acres where it runs free.

It is this space requirement, unobtainable in most zoos, which prevents the cheetah from being bred in captivity with any degree of success in the view of Dr. Anthony Harthoorn, Physiology Department head at Nairobi's University College. He believes they may have powerful territorial instincts which require large areas before breeding can take place.

For many years zoo directors believed it impossible to furnish the necessary environment and enough space to captive cheetahs to encourage breeding. For some species the presence of people or other animals interrupted or prevented the mating ritual which often is complicated with many steps prior to mating. Some needed special foods found only in natural habitats. The necessary ingredients for captive breeding of such wildlife as gorillas, flamingoes, boas and cheetahs were beyond man's understanding. In recent years, however, the store of knowledge has increased significantly. Almost all captive species can be furnished the environments they need for normal behavior.

In 1966, a cheetah in the Rome Zoo gave birth to three cubs, Rip, Nembo and Gero. The cheetah mother was as proud as any domestic housecat of her young and seemed to be pleased with the playing and petting given them by their supervisor, Dr. L. Spinelli. Two other zoos, England's Southport Zoo and one in Germany, have also had recent successful cheetah births.

What is the cheetah's future in its natural habitat? Is it headed for early extinction as most casual wildlife students believe?

Because of its habit of not returning to a half-eaten carcass like the lion or leopard the cheetah was once condemned as a wasteful killer. Thirty-eight cheetahs were shot on sight in one African park as a result of this early conservation effort. Finally the short-sightedness of this viewpoint was realized and cheetah shooting was stopped.

Since it was seldom seen by observers who saw lions in ample numbers it was assumed that the reason for this discrepancy was the rapid decline of cheetah numbers. A similar logic supports the belief that cattle herds on East African plains have driven the wild herds into near extinction. In reality there are areas where there is more wildlife now than there has been for decades, or for centuries in the case of managed wildlife areas.

Cheetah numbers show no present tendency to decline. The East African Wildlife Society sponsored a cheetah survey which covered the period from 1960 to 1965. Over 1,200 sightings were analyzed to prevent duplications in count. "Nothing was found," reported one of the surveyors, A. Graham, "during the survey to suggest that the animal is declining or that population densities are lower now than they were, except possibly in the Narok district of Kenya." In East Africa the cheetah can be seen in an area of 406,000 square miles.

3: *The Lion, Hunter and Hunted*

ONE OF THE REAL SURPRISES FOR THE FIRST-TIME VISITOR to a big game reserve in East or South Africa is the tolerance of lions toward vehicles. It seems almost unbelievable that these huge cats feeding on a carcass killed moments before will pay little or no attention to vehicles driving to within a few steps and parking while its occupants observe and photograph without fear of molestation.

Like most wildlife, lions in protected areas have learned quickly that they have nothing to fear from these vehicles which reek of oil and gas fumes. The human scent is eclipsed by these engine smells and as long as the occupants remain reasonably quiet without excessive movement the lions pay no attention to the vehicles. Cubs have been observed playing with the warm automobile tires while their mother rested a few steps away.

This situation has lulled more than one visitor into a false sense of security. All the parks and reserves have notices warning visitors to stay in their vehicles but like the signs in American parks warning visitors not to feed the bears these are sometimes disregarded.

A few years ago one American couple stopped near a lion pride and the husband decided he wanted a photograph with the lions behind him. He stepped to the ground and posed. His wife tried to focus her camera but had trouble finding him in the viewfinder. She looked up. He was lying on the ground, killed by a single swipe from the lion which had come up behind him.

C. T. Astley Maberly, who has studied and observed African lions in the wild over a period of thirty-three years, says that lions usually look at approaching vehicles intently but very quickly lose interest in these large objects with their inanimate smells. However, as soon as a person opens a door and separates himself from the vehicle the lion recognizes him as a human being immediately. The fact that the person materializes suddenly from nowhere accentuates whatever instinctive fear the lion may have. He is apt to attack quickly in self-defense.

The danger is far greater to a man who makes a surprise appearance from an unsuspected place such as a motor vehicle, than if the man were to accidentally confront the lion in the brush where the lion might have at least a minimum of forewarning.

Alexander Lake pointed out some of the mistakes of fourteen dead lion hunters in his book, *Killers in Africa*. Four died while running from a lion, thus inviting attention to themselves and encouraging attack, a response to be expected from most predators, even small yard dogs. Some believed that the shock from a poorly-aimed large caliber bullet would stop a lion, an unfortunate assumption. Some initiated charges by talking at a critical moment, the sound infuriating an otherwise disinterested lion. Some followed wounded lions before the wounds had a chance to slow the lion's response. Some were hysterical at the critical moment. Some depended on missing gun bearers. Six of those hunters mentioned by Lake are buried at Nairobi; the others, at scattered sites. All grave markers symbolize the fury of disturbed lions. No knowledgeable hunter takes a chance with this animal that has been called the king of beasts.

Dr. Bernhard Grzimek, one of the world's best known zoologists because of his efforts in promoting African wildlife conservation, once decided to see what would happen if he did step from a vehicle near a lion. Driving to within eight yards of a lion he found that the lion typically ignored the vehicle. "When I opened the door and started to get out," he reported in his book, *Serengeti Shall Not Die,* "the lion rose, snarled, spat and came towards me. I naturally disappeared back inside the car again."

There are exceptions to the expected lion-vehicle relationship. Occasionally a honeymooning, or perhaps confused, lion has hit a vehicle with all its power. Safari hunter J. A. Hunter was driving a three-ton truck in Kenya when a lion charged the truck, leaping the final ten feet and hitting the truck hard enough to make it shudder. Stopping the truck Hunter took his rifle and stepped around behind the vehicle. A disillusioned lion was walking away from the metal monster.

The lion seems to be the most unconcerned of all cats about potential hazards to himself. He displays none of the nervousness of the smaller cats, such as the leopard, African wildcat, caracal and serval. The chief behavior characteristic that impresses the casual observer and biologist alike is his laziness. Apparently the lion sleeps or naps about eighteen hours a day, hunting or observing most of the remaining time. Eating takes little time. Zoo observations have shown lions to be active from one to a maximum of seven hours a day. In contrast a zoo elephant may sleep or rest as little as one hour in each twenty-four.

I have seen no animal or person who could fall asleep so quickly. One morning on Ngorongoro's floor I watched a black-maned lion stalk out of the papyrus marsh and sit down between two vehicles parked about fifty yards apart. The lion sat there, or lay there, as if posing grandly for a sculptor carving a suitable symbol for some magnificent building. Not once did he look at either vehicle.

Suddenly, without any indication of his intention, he literally flopped to his side, so quickly that his mane bounced on impact. His eyes were closed tight before his mane settled. He never moved and I had the im-

Young male Lion

pression he was snoring soundly when we moved shortly away.

It takes no particular perception to recognize a lion about to charge. The posture is the same as any angry housecat. Ears flatten as the lion crouches and curls his tail from side to side. As a lion's anger increases the tail jerks up and down and the charge begins with a trot. The flattened ears show most specifically the state of anger. If they are still cocked erect even when the tail whips about the lion is excited and perhaps curious, but they do not indicate anger.

The alert system in the African wilderness is as varied as it is effective. Small birds may watch a lion stalk toward them for a considerable time. Then the lion crosses a safe boundary line and the birds leap into the air screaming. The action startles a monkey. Its movement catches an antelope's eye. Its grunt sends the herd fleeing. The wilderness alert system seems more dependable in Africa than most other places because of the numbers and diversity of wildlife. Each sudden movement or voice is repeated and rebroadcast sometimes for miles.

It seems that most wildlife has a far better perception of hostile intent or lack of it in neighboring animals or humans than man does. African hoofed animals will allow predators to move close and even among themselves without bolting if they detect none of the indications of a beginning hunt. This awareness may result from nothing more than recognizing a stiffer walk or half-lifted ears. All the characteristics of hunting predators seem to be well-known to the herbivores and they take evasive action accordingly. The hunted seem also to be aware of certain characteristics in their hunters and react accordingly.

A single lion attacking more than one buffalo is the nearest thing to suicide a lion can devise. One observer saw a lion in his prime, but overeager because of hunger, attack two buffalo. The individual selected for the target stopped suddenly as the lion jumped, thus causing the lion to miss completely. When it sailed past and sprawled, the buffalo pair leaped forward, one hooking the lion and holding him down while the other ripped it open. Then both buffalo began the often-reported but seldom-pictured ritual of obliteration. They literally pounded the lion into the ground. When they had finished their furious effort there were no recognizable lion parts left, but only the bloody, churned soil.

A lion in Murchison Falls National Park tried to ambush a buffalo not far from the Paraa Lodge. The buffalo was not intimidated. Its horns did effective work and the lion died before the buffalo's fury diminished. Crocodiles ate most of the lion during the night. In the same park a warden watched a small buffalo herd chasing three lions which had just killed two hartebeests and were trying to eat them. The buffalo kept the lions away from their kills for over an hour.

At the neighboring Queen Elizabeth National Park a lioness pounced on a hippo calf and killed it. Before she could begin eating, however, two hippo females killed her.

In February, 1965 Syd Downey, a veteran game man of East Africa, stopped his vehicle near a pride of nineteen lions which had just killed a buffalo. As the lions ate, the dead buffalo's companions waited only a few yards away, watching the lions but taking no defensive or retaliatory action. They seemed to recognize that potential danger to themselves had passed. None of the lions gave any indication of interest in anything other than eating the dead buffalo. If the herd had been excited or concerned they could have chased the lions away.

Lion-buffalo relationships seem to be always based on the situation at the moment. Not far from the spot where Downey saw the buffalo watching their companion being eaten, observers in Uganda's Queen Elizabeth National Park saw three lions fleeing a herd of about 300 buffalo. The two lionesses turned aside into tall grass and the lion turned and ran at the buffalo. The buffalo reversed their direction and allowed themselves to be chased momentarily. Then one buffalo turned on the lion and chased him into the grass where the lionesses had disappeared.

One hunter saw a lioness stalking a buffalo. She gathered her hind legs to spring and her tail stiffened straight. Suddenly a lion roared beyond the buffalo and as the lion reared to swat the buffalo's face the lioness leaped upon its flank. The buffalo whirled to knock the lion flat with its front feet. Ignoring the clawing lioness it dropped to its knees, thrust its head aside and shoved a horn into the lion's chest.

Then the buffalo shook the lioness off but she leaped upon it again. The hunter shot her off this time and the buffalo whirled into the brush and disappeared.

Alexander Lake, examining spoor around three battle scenes that resulted in a dead buffalo and one or more dead lions, found that two lions had jumped one buffalo, three lions, another and five, another. In none of the cases had the surviving lions touched the carcass. Bloody spoor indicated that some of the lions were fortunate to get away.

Surprisingly the buffalo is the main item on the menu for Zambian lions. In the two main game areas of the Luangwa Valley and Kafue National Park it is an exceptional circumstance when any prey other than buffalo is taken according to Kafue's former warden, Norman Carr. In contrast a buffalo kill in other parts of Africa's lion country is so rare as to cause special attention in game reports and newspapers. In East and South Africa, wildebeests are by far the most popular prey, followed by zebra and antelope.

Carr does not credit lions with hunting tactics that show reasoning as defined by man. He believes that when a lion moves upwind of game to stampede it toward waiting members of the hunting party, it is

not preplanned but is misinterpreted by human observers. He believes that such flushing by upwind lion
scent is coincidental. Lions spread out and position
themselves to get a good position from which to attack
when the potential prey is vulnerable.

Carr witnessed a number of lion attacks on buffalo.
He watched five lions move downwind of a small
buffalo herd and settle into the grass to wait for the
herd to move closer. After a long interval the buffalo
moved toward the water near which the lions waited.
When a buffalo approached within seventy yards a
lioness launched her attack. She sprang and sunk her
teeth into the buffalo's neck.

The buffalo fled with the lioness holding her position. Another lioness came to her support, slapping a
paw across the buffalo's face and pulling the head
down. The buffalo stumbled and fell. Two young
lions kept up feints against the remaining members of
the herd, the tactic effectively keeping them from
coming to the aid of the stricken buffalo if such had
been their intent. Whether the feints were done
deliberately to distract the herd or not, the effect was
the same.

There seem to be substantial exceptions to the expected lion-prey relationship. Most smaller hoofed
animals can be expected to run for their lives when a
lion bursts after them. However, some do not. Attacking lions have been wounded or killed by such antelopes as eland, oryx (gemsbok), and wildebeest. The

wildebeest has a reputation for pugnacity at times and if a clean kill is not made quickly the attacker may be put to flight.

Lions are versatile in their menu. If there were more powerful animals which preyed on Africa's hoofed animals, the lion might be little more than a scavenger, pushing the hyena down the line one more place. It has no aversion to carrion, even the most overwhelmingly repulsive in man's viewpoint. It wastes little prey after it is taken. Unless driven off by a hyena pack or for some other reason, a lion or pride guards the prey and eats from it over a period of hours or days until all the edible parts are consumed.

Because of its casual menu the lion does not hesitate to take lesser animals if its favored zebra, wildebeest or other antelopes are not available. Significant numbers of wart hogs are taken. Baboons, pythons, young elephants, hippos and rhinos are also killed. A large pride will sometimes take a giraffe in its prime. One observer saw a lioness miss an antelope and shortly stalk bush doves feeding on the ground. She slapped two of them down as the flock took wing.

The powerful lion is not a clean killer. Some veteran naturalists of lion country believe that the majority of kills results from strangulation, not from the prey's throat being ripped open and the jugular vein severed. Lion teeth seldom penetrate the thick skin of antelopes, zebra and buffalo during the kill.

The Ngorongoro Crater has an unusual ratio of

hyenas to adult lions, about 600 hyenas to a dozen adult lions in 1965. The scraps from lion kills are inadequate to support this large hyena population. As a result, the hyenas often become pure predators, dragging down wildebeests and zebras, usually in packs organized for the moment of competing individuals rather than of cooperating individuals. Occasionally a single hyena will attack healthy, large antelopes or zebras.

The wildebeest has an unfortunate behavior habit which insures that many more bulls (as high as eighty percent of the total) than female wildebeests are killed as prey. The bulls have a strong territorial instinct and station themselves on a selected spot of ground from which they drive other bull wildebeests but to which they welcome any passing female wildebeest. On the Ngorongoro Crater floor with its 25,000 wildebeests in a circle roughly ten miles across, solitary bulls can be seen easily. They stand in the open well away from bushes which might conceal them from predators. Consequently, they are taken with some regularity.

One October morning I saw a wildebeest bull running at full speed about his territory, apparently headed for a stream extending from the shallow crater lake. I could not see what chased him because of high grass. A few minutes later, however, I did see the result. We had to drive up the stream a half mile or so before we could cross it. We drove down the opposite bank.

The wildebeest bull had gotten to within ten yards of the stream's high bank before the hyenas dragged him down. Eight hyenas with bobbing, wary heads, literally tore him apart before twice as many more came loping through the grass to share the feast.

Do lions and other predators talk to each other and make plans the way people do? Yes, it appears that they do. Perhaps eyes convey far more meaning to companions than the most expressive human eyes can do. Without a doubt voice communications: grunts, coughs, snarls, purrs and a variety of other sounds, tell companions what is on a lion's mind.

Few observers have or take the time to know the wilderness intimately enough to be on hand when a lion hunt or other animal drama begins and is carried to an end.

Warden Varaday and his game scout watched a bachelor pride of five hold a council of war one afternoon. Two of the lions rested near bushes containing a reclining buffalo pair. The two lions summoned with soft grunts the other three. The three came immediately. After a few moments of instructions the five divided into tactical units.

One experienced male and a pair of young adults walked out to the left and toward the thicket containing the buffalo. The other two lions walked to the right and toward the thicket to pause in a natural drainage ditch. One lay down behind the other. Both held their heads high to look for movement.

Shortly the three-lion unit entered the thicket, attacked the buffalo pair, and emerged with one lion on each buffalo. The other lion had already been killed. The bucking buffalo with poorly-positioned riders headed toward the lion pair waiting in ambush. One buffalo tossed its rider into a thorn bush, spotted the ambushing pair and shoved the other buffalo away into a new direction. The second lion was dislodged by a tree limb and the two buffalo sent the unsuccessful riders into a hasty retreat. The waiting lions were powerless to take effective action and watched the buffalo lope off without further interference.

Young lions of both sexes are awkward, bumbling hunters at best, even young males weighing more than their mothers. The training is extensive but many hunts are ruined by impatient young ones charging prematurely or making some other wrong move. Many times a lioness will bring down the prey and as her young pile on she backs away to let them finish the job. Then the prey, even a wildebeest calf, shakes itself free and runs away.

So conditioned are lions to one-time attacks in a hunt that they practically never follow up if the prey is not caught in the initial rush, or if it breaks away and flees.

It would appear that a young adult male old enough to contest the pride leader's position should be old enough to take care of itself. This is not always the case. Such a young adult, expelled from the pride after losing a fight with the patriarch, finds itself suddenly on its own. Up until this hour the young male had only a small part to play in taking game. Other members of the pride coordinated the hunt and usually downed the prey in concert. Now with no other lion to assist the young male finds itself frustrated at every turn. Overeagerness generated by hunger alerts prey too soon. Ineptness in seizing the prey is likely to be ineffective.

One ranger watched such a young male attack a zebra, his eagerness directing him to the herd's stallion. The lion sprang to the zebra's shoulder but was quickly bucked free. The zebra kicked out furiously with hind feet, hitting the lion in the stomach with such force that the next sighting of the lion, twenty miles away the following day, showed him to be still groaning from the kick.

One young lion making a brash attack on a giraffe calf received the surprise of his life when the mother giraffe intercepted and seriously injured him by swinging her head down to deflect him. Although lions do occasionally take adult giraffes these huge awkward-appearing animals are better able to take care of themselves than most hoofed animals. One full-grown lioness rushing at a giraffe was struck first with the giraffe's front feet, then given a mortal blow with the rear hoofs. A later look at the dead lioness showed the top of her head literally opened by the giraffe's kick.

As might be imagined from the lion's size it needs a substantial amount of meat. Computations by researchers in East Africa show that lions kill one to one and a half pounds of prey for each ten pounds of their body weight daily. Although a kill may not be made each day the average daily kill amounts to this figure. Thus a 300-pound lion will kill thirty to forty-five pounds of prey daily or five to eight tons annually. One estimate calculates that lions kill about three times as much prey as they actually eat. The meat not eaten by lions is consumed by the scavengers.

The lion's strength is amazing. J. A. Hunter, doing control work for the Kenyan Game Department in 1925, examined a thorn fence, or boma, twelve feet high around a Masai village. The night before his arrival a lion jumped it, killed a cow, threw it partially over its shoulder while holding the cow's throat and leaped out again. The lion weighed about 400 pounds; the cow about 800.

Although some parts of Africa still abound with game as measured by wildlife populations in other parts of the world, not many decades ago many sections of Africa were infested with wildlife. The term infested is used deliberately because such high populations swung violently from superabundance in years of good rain to devastation in times of drought and epidemic. One savanna might nurture animals num-

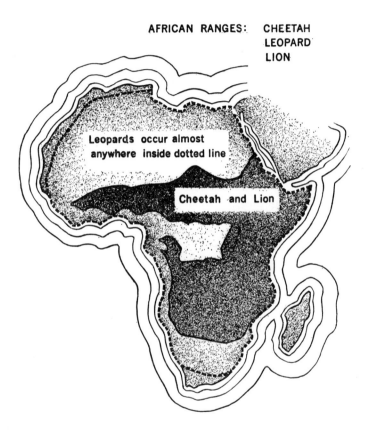

AFRICAN RANGES: CHEETAH
LEOPARD
LION

Leopards occur almost
anywhere inside dotted line

Cheetah and Lion

bered in the hundreds of thousands and a few years later be a dusty, barren desert with no big game.

J. A. Hunter told of a foot safari between Arusha, Tanganyika (now Tanzania) and Ngorongoro Crater after an outbreak of rinderpest. The few surviving animals were skin and bones, he reported, and the plains were strewn with bleached bones. Porters threatened to turn back because they were provided no meat. The area today has a fairly stabilized ratio of small farms and Masai herds, as well as important big game populations both inside and beyond the borders of game reserves and national parks.

Africans struggling to make a living by subsistence farming or with small herds of stock led a dangerous existence under the constant threat of uncowed wild animals. If this situation is hard to visualize, one has only to visit some of the bush country villages still raided by elephants or other big game populations. Then it will be easy enough to picture the insecurity of human life among herds and prides significantly larger.

In the mid-1920's, after a rinderpest plague had decimated Kenya's wild herds, the huge lion population turned to Masai cattle herds for food. The situation became serious immediately. Although the Masai were proud to the point of arrogance of their own abilities in killing lions with spears, they were no match for the overwhelming lion raids on their herds. Kenya's game department hired professional hunter and guide, J. A. Hunter, to thin the lion populations in the Masai areas, giving him the valuable skins of all lions he shot. He had three months to do the job.

Hunter went to work, training his own pack of lion dogs from mongrels purchased from the Nairobi dog pound. The dogs developed quickly into adequate lion chasers after several of the overeager dogs were flattened by their prey. Masai warriors came to Hunter after his first kill to bring him to their own areas where he could hunt cattle-killing lions. Shortly he found himself doing all the hunting he could manage, setting up ambush sites over Masai herdsmen and cattle killed by the lions.

He killed three lions one evening outside a Masai village. Within a few weeks he had taken seventy lions, but still the Masai were bringing him reports of lion depredations. A climax to this intensive game control operation came when he shot eighteen lions from a boma, or thorn enclosure, one night while an old Masai man held a flashlight on his targets. He returned to Nairobi with the skins of eighty-eight lions and ten leopards.

Such cycles of game overabundance will return. Older Nairobi citizens knew such men as Leslie Simpson, an American who shot 365 lions in one year during the early 1900's. Lions then were considered in the same class of vermin as a brown rat is today in a slum tenement.

There will be periods of too few lions. Fortunately

improving game management skills are smoothing these volatile ups and downs which have afflicted every African civilization. It is popular to condemn modern man for decimating some animal populations. Such incidents are extremely rare when compared to the protective hand he has extended over endangered wildlife populations.

It is very doubtful that Africa's lion population or those of the prey animals will ever dip to the unrecorded low points from epidemic and starvation which Africa's Stone Age culture witnessed.

4: *Pride Life*

THE PRIDE, OR FAMILY CLAN, IS THE BASIS OF LION society and seldom are adult outsiders admitted to it. The pride may begin with a lioness and a pair of cubs. When she comes into season again one or more lions will join her from a neighboring pride. During hunts she may take her cubs to one or more neighboring prides. A pride is always changing its composition. As many as thirty lions have been observed in one pride, especially when game is scarce and additional numbers raise the rate of hunting success.

Strangely a honeymoon for lions is similar to that for people. A lioness and one or more lions will drop out of pride life and remain in one place which appeals to them for days. They eat little or nothing during this time and the lion's patience is short. He is always ready to chase off an intruder, another unacceptable lion, another species, and on occasion a vehicle. Part of this effort seems to be a display for the benefit of the lioness. When an intruder approaches the male's hackles lift. He growls and whips his tail from side to side. He may make short rushes at a vehicle, a display which is usually successful.

Experienced observers say the lioness during this period delights in trying her partner's patience. If she sees another male she may walk directly to the newcomer until her furious partner drives him away, or is driven off himself. Occasionally a honeymooning lioness will walk close to a vehicle and stretch out beside it, a tactic which is wearing on her partner's nerves, especially when the vehicle fails to move.

Man's most flagrant excursions into anthropomorphism, or humanizing animals, occurs when he assigns the moralities of a particular human culture to animals. There was a time a few decades ago when nature writers spoke indignantly of certain animal species with loose morals and no family responsibilities. A lion who mated and wandered off to find another mate shortly was considered a poor example as a "father."

This was completely ridiculous, of course. Very few animal species have life habits which resemble those of our own. There is no such thing as animal morality, or good and bad, in animal behavior.

The lion, or male, is often pictured as a lazy bully or brute, who lets the female do the hunting. Then he rushes in to eat first. The lioness and her cubs eat what is left.

This hunting method has been observed often enough to lead many to believe that the "martyred" lioness always does the killing for the "shiftless" lions of the pride and vicinity. This is not a true picture.

As young lions reach maturity they are forced out of the pride by the possessive older lion or lions and they must make their own way independently. They form bachelor prides and live together for indefinite periods. In the same way overage lions are forced out during courtship fights. Occasionally a young male will join forces with such an oldster and the two will hunt together successfully.

Does the lioness derive any benefit from an overbearing lion sharing her kill? It appears that she does. Richard Estes, studying Ngorongoro wildebeest one night through an infrared telescope watched twenty hyenas kill a wildebeest bull which two lionesses had chased first. The hyenas had rushed in and the lionesses tried to ward them off thus enabling the wildebeest to get away from the lionesses but not the hyenas.

After the hyenas had started eating, the lionesses crept close but did not dare contest the prize. Then a lion rushed from the darkness, scattering the hyenas. He picked up the kill and carried it across a stream. Eventually he ate part of it and left the remainder to the waiting lionesses.

It would take an unfeeling individual not to be captivated by lion cubs playing with their mother and assorted males in prides which may number as many as thirty individuals. The mother drops out of the pride most of the time to have her cubs, seeking privacy and cover while the cubs are almost helpless.

Although the gestation period is only 105 days the lioness does not breed but once about every two years because her cubs are not self-sufficient until about eighteen months old.

Two to four cubs comprise the normal lion litter. These are usually born in thick brush, grass or reeds where the mother can make herself a bed to her liking, differing little in this respect from other members of the cat family including the domestic housecat. Births take place at any time of the year.

Cubs' eyes are partially open at birth but clear vision does not come for a week. When only a few weeks old the cubs instinctively seize meat brought by the mother and "attack" it energetically with much growling. These activities look more violent than they are and any prey not killed by the mother is apt to pull free and escape, even an African hare smaller than the cubs.

Cooperation gives the lion an advantage not accorded the cheetah. Frequently another lioness will baby-sit for cubs while the mother is hunting. This accounts for the occasional sightings of a lioness with cubs of obvious differences in age. As a result of this care the lion cub has less to fear from hyena raids which are so devastating to unguarded cheetah litters.

The lioness is a devoted mother. It takes an unusual event to separate her from her cubs, and even in the most critical emergency she seizes at least one cub by the scruff of the neck and rushes it to safety.

Alan Tarlton recently told *Africana* Magazine readers of shooting nuisance lions on the family's East African ranch in 1928. After one such hunt he brought home a tiny lion cub of the same size, color and age as two ranch pups. The three young animals struck up a fast friendship which lasted for several weeks.

One evening after a rain the adult dogs suddenly disappeared upwind chasing an unseen animal. The next morning he checked the tracks and found that an adult lion had moved upwind of the ranch to attract the dogs while the cub's mother rushed in and ripped open the cage which held her young one. The two pups loped off with their friend.

Days later Tarlton saw the pups and cub headed back toward the ranch. He called. The pups came to him but the cub turned and ran back into the brush. The pups seemed in excellent health from their diet of raw meat and lion milk but one died later of tick-fever caused by the premature introduction to raw meat.

The lion mother with new cubs is an extremely dangerous animal and will attack almost any threat to her litter. Because lionesses seek the most shaded, peaceful spots along cool rivers to lie with her cubs the African national parks are strict about visitors stepping out of their cars. The most pleasantly shady spot a person would choose for a picnic may have been selected by a lion mother for her daytime sleeping site.

The new cubs have their mother's golden tan coloration with white underparts plus a liberal sprinkling of spots aligned in irregular rows which give the cub something of a brindled appearance. These spots fade gradually but usually can be seen long after the young lion reaches adult weights. The tail tuft, which is a characteristic not shared with any other feline, is present at birth, although of insignificant size.

When the cubs are about three months old the lioness rejoins the pride. Over the next few months the cubs are exposed to their most critical source of danger, the feeding males. Unless the mother is constantly watchful her cubs will rush up to an excited male on freshly-killed prey and receive a fatal blow or bite. At other times when males are stuffed and relaxed they are tolerant toward the annoying cubs, warding off mock attacks with sheathed claws. After these periods of rough play the male may groom the nearest youngster for extended periods by licking its fur with a rough tongue.

The lion's tongue has an amazing rasping quality. A single tongue swipe across a person's face may be enough to lacerate the skin severely. A favorite activity of feeding lions after initial hunger has been satisfied with the prey's internal organs, is to lick the inner walls of the body cavity. The meat there comes off in minute slivers with each tongue swipe and the ribs are soon sanded clean of meat.

African game men can identify from a pile of bones what feeding order occurred. A wildebeest skeleton picked clean with few bones disturbed except the cartilage at rib ends was probably the victim of lions only. If little was left of the skeleton except cracked bones and the horns the carcass was worked over by hyenas whose powerful jaws cracked the bones so the marrow could be obtained.

During cubhood the lioness takes every opportunity to train her young. Smaller prey is seldom killed outright but held struggling while the excited cubs pounce on it and administer multiple bites ineffectually. Occasionally the lioness allows the prey to struggle erect and make a limited escape from her awkward young ones. It takes many such training sessions for the young to learn the technique necessary for quick overpowering of antelopes and larger hoofed animals.

The young lion's milk teeth are retained until it is about a year old when they are replaced by permanent teeth. At this age the young lion begins participating in game drives and stalks.

These coordinated hunts are executed with obvious planning and skill. When the prey is sighted the lionesses and an occasional lion move downwind, taking care to remain concealed. One or more lions move upwind until his scent drifts down to the prey animals which bolt downwind away from this obvious danger. As the fleeing prey comes within a few yards of a waiting lioness she rushes for the selected individual. If she miscalculates and is unable to overtake it within fifty to one hundred yards, she usually gives up the chase as a bad effort.

Surprise is the key to success in a lion hunt as it is with the other cats. The lion does not have staying power in an extended chase. If the prey cannot be seized within a few yards, it usually escapes unharmed.

Perhaps the most detailed survey of East African lions was made by Game Warden George Adamson, whose wife Joy wrote the universally popular *Born Free* and its sequels. Over a period of three and a half months he traveled daily over parts of a 2,000 square-mile portion of the Serengeti Plains. He arrived at a lion population of 450 individuals for this area, tabulating three times as many lionesses over three years old as lions. There were twice as many cubs under six months as cubs over six months, and twice as many young lions eighteen months to three years of age as lionesses.

He was struck by the restricted territory of each pride, "much more conservative than is generally supposed," he reported. Prides seldom moved more than five or six miles in any one direction, even during shifts of zebra and wildebeest herds which migrated.

Because of his personal experience with Elsa which his wife reared, George Adamson was alert to reactions by lion prides to visits by strange lions. Did lions accept outsiders, or would they tolerate only known members or former members of the pride?

One day he watched two lionesses and a young

lion begin stalking a small zebra herd. The stalk was progressing well until another lioness walked in from another direction and spooked the zebra.

"The stranger was received coldly," reported Adamson, "with none of the customary head-rubbings which takes place between lions who are acquainted. The four sat down together, apparently in mutual tolerance, but suddenly without any warning the original three turned on the stranger; she was bowled over and had to flee for her life, being pursued for a considerable distance."

Adamson believes that a successful release of tame or even wild lions is exceedingly difficult. A lion under two years of age is incapable of killing efficiently and sufficiently to provide for itself. Of greatest danger to the newly-released lion are lion prides already established in the territory who would probably cripple it in fights and render it almost completely incapable of taking care of itself.

The only possibility of a reasonable chance of survival for such a lion, once removed by distance, time or accident from its pride and home territory is for the lion to be released in an area without lions or humans but with enough game to allow the lion to establish itself. Unfortunately enough game would attract other lions.

Adamson believes that a lion released under the age of one year stands no chance of survival. Strangely a cub under eight weeks of age might be accepted by a foster lion mother if it is not picked up by a hyena or other predator first.

Perhaps the most successful return of lion pets to the wild was accomplished by Norman Carr. Born in Africa of British parents, Carr became the first warden of Kafue National Park when it opened in 1957 as Africa's largest park. Shortly he became a foster father to lion cubs when one of his rangers had to shoot a charging lioness and orphaned her two cubs. Both were males and lived with him for the next four years, acting like boisterous kittens much of the time. Many of these play periods were strenuous since he weighed 140 pounds and each lion weighed 400.

He learned their moods and never went near them when they were feeding or irritable. Consequently, he never was in serious danger from his gigantic pets. They roamed freely over his camp and by the time they were four years old Carr decided to return them to the wild. After many trips into the wild observing his pets taking prey, Carr left them.

Each time he did this, however, they returned to camp. He would chase them away. They returned again and sprawled at his feet to nap. Finally he hauled them 100 miles away and hoped that they could survive. Almost a year later he found that they had been accepted by a pride and were healthy. He drove to the area where he left them and spotted both eating with a pride.

Carr called to his former pets. They had always

come to him immediately when he kept them at his camp. The largest ex-pet looked up from his eating and walked toward Carr. It stopped 125 yards away and looked over his foster father. The relationship was a thing of the past. He turned and walked back to his meal.

What should happen to a lion reared by people? If the lion has a choice about it, I strongly suspect he would choose a comfortable zoo in almost any large city in the world. Of many lions I have observed and photographed in Africa the healthiest, most contented live in the Johannesburg Zoo, one of the world's most beautiful. One hitch in such plans, however, is to find a zoo of any size which does not have lions coming out of its ears. Lions are so contented in zoos that the steady supply of cubs soon becomes a liability. Other zoos are seldom willing to exchange animals for lion cubs. They usually have an oversupply also.

The lion is not a beautiful animal when compared to most of the other cat family members, especially when he is close. Because he is essentially a ground-dwelling animal the lion is a scruffy, seedy, indolent mammal. At close range most mature lions are poorly-groomed and often well-scarred about the face from fights within the pride. The lion's proudest mark, at least in man's eyes, is its mane. When the mane is thick and full it normally is as full of seed burs as an un-combed cocker spaniel. I took photos of the black-maned males which make Ngorongoro Crater famous as lion habitat, shooting rapidly as these huge lions stalked from the papyrus marshes and paying no attention to details. Later when I studied the transparencies I saw an unbelievable collection of seeds, mud balls and knots in the "magnificent" mane.

These lions I recorded on film were in their prime. Average males are something less than these. In hot, dry areas lions have manes which are little more than a scruffy collar of hair around the neck. Some lions of Kenya's Tsavo National Park have almost no mane at all.

The mane is not necessarily the distinguishing mark of lions seen in the field. Traditionally the ideal lion has had a huge mane, preferably black, covering the entire neck and forming a heavy ruff between the shoulder blades. Actually the mane is usually something less than this and may be no more than a short ruff around the neck. Some lions are practically maneless. All male lions have a cheek ruff of longer hair. The lioness does not grow this cheek ruff.

There are enough distinguishing physical characteristics among African lions to allow the identification of several races. The Barbary lion, *Felis leo leo,* is from North Africa. It is large, yellow and has a thick mane. The Senegal lion, *Felis leo senegalensis,* occurs from Senegal to the eastern Sudan. It is a reddish-yellow lion of medium size with a small mane. The Cape lion, *Felis leo melanochaitus,* is a muddy-yellow animal larger than the Barbary lion with a bushy, black mane.

The Masai lion, *Felis leo massaica,* is the typical East African lion with yellowish mane. The Somali lion, *Felis leo somaliensis,* tends to be the smallest African lion. Its mane is slight but its ears are large and its tail is long.

An experienced tracker can tell at a glance the sex of most lions whose tracks he sees. The lion has much larger forepaws than hind paws and significantly larger than those of the lioness.

Although lions are called Africa's king of beasts they are not as big as often supposed. A large lion seldom reaches 400 pounds hungry. After stuffing himself he may reach 500 pounds, considerably less than such animals as the black bear with which Americans are more familiar. American black bears—stuffed for the winter rest—have been weighed at over 700 pounds. A large lioness weighs about 300 pounds.

It would take an exceptional lion to measure nine feet six inches from nose to tail tip. Most lions measure under nine feet. One British hunter-naturalist, Colonel Stevenson-Hamilton measured 150 lions during his experiences in Africa. Only one of these approached ten feet in length. Shoulder heights for lions vary from about forty inches to forty-five inches. Those for lionesses average about thirty-four inches.

Some of the most common things about lions and other animals often are the most complex to analyze. One of these is the lion's roar.

Naturalists do not agree on its purpose. The trouble

lies in the fact that one observer sees a lion and hears it roar to scare game; another man sees a roaring lion apparently calling to other pride members; another sees a roar used to flush scavengers from its kill and perhaps another sees a lion pride designating its territory for the benefit of potential intruders by roaring. Each observer is inclined to feel a lion's roar is due to the circumstance he personally observed. None would be wrong, there are so many circumstances under which lions roar.

I once heard zoo lions roaring with such excitement that I could feel my neck tingle. A keeper was dispensing fresh meat to the various inhabitants of the lion house.

Game biologist Richard Estes, who has studied lion behavior extensively in Ngorongoro, doubts that lions roar to frighten game. He has watched the herds there remain unshaken by lion roars, even recordings played from forty yards away. Perhaps the high concentrations of prey and predators alike here make a difference. Prey animals hear lion roars so often in this natural basin that they become accustomed to them. Then there is the additional security for each zebra or wildebeest since it has a huge herd of companions in which it can lose itself. I suspect that a lion's roar in an area of small herds and infrequent lion roars and sightings has an entirely different effect.

The amount of deliberate cooperation which goes into a lion hunt is not sufficiently understood. However, the results of many hunts suggest the tactics were not a matter of chance, but were caused by the exact position and actions of the individuals in the group. Cattle in pens have been stampeded out by a lion walking upwind and roaring while the lionesses waited downwind to ambush the frightened cattle.

I spent one night in a tent camp on the plains of southern Kenya which was used as a sanctuary by a young zebra. It roamed freely among the tents to graze but stayed away from the thorn fence which protected one side of the camp. As the night cooled from the air sliding off nearby mountains, a lion moved past the camp upwind and roared every few steps. I have wondered if his reason was to frighten the zebra out of the tent area into range of the lionesses waiting downwind.

Recently I had spent a long day photographing below Kilimanjaro and I was tired. At the Amboseli tent camp a campfire attracted all my companions but I headed for my tent alone. It took only moments for me to shed boots and clothes and slide between warm blankets since most East African nights are cool to cold.

I relaxed immediately. The tent flap zipper was tied to keep out the everpresent vervet monkeys which stole anything they could carry. The tent was insect proof. It was too cold for snakes or millipedes or any other cold-blooded creature to move about. I thought briefly of these things and took some comfort in these facts. My eyes closed.

At that moment the most explosive roar I have ever imagined reverberated from behind the tent. I say reverberated because I was literally shaken into a sitting position.

I had watched a Yellowstone bear draw a single claw down a tent side, opening its own zipper in a quick swipe. I waited for a lion paw to do the same as roar followed roar. A man had been dragged by a lion from a tent on the Serengeti Plains not too long before. He had been killed quickly.

The tent side swayed ever so slightly. Finally enough reason returned to make me realize that the breeze was doing it.

The next roar was a few yards farther away. Or perhaps I hoped so. As I lay there with blankets gripped tightly over my head mentally trying my best to turn off all the scent glands which might give me away, I gradually realized that the lion was moving farther away.

Finally I remembered that Africa's traditional lion barrier, the thorn fence, passed just behind the tent. I really had no idea how far away the lion had been, but as I thought about it later I am confident it was on the other side.

I never knew what set off the roaring. If I could allow the lion a human quality or two, I wonder if that lion had slipped up quietly to us unsuspecting outsiders, set off its hair-raising routine and walked away with a grin on its face.

Chances are my lion roared from enthusiasm with no real reason other than it just felt like roaring.

So why does a lion roar? For all the reasons we have discussed, but no single reason.

5: *Man-Eating Lions*

NONE OF AFRICA'S MAN-EATING LIONS HAVE ACHIEVED
the notoriety or generated such fright as a pair of
lions known as the man-eaters of Tsavo. The area in
southeastern Kenya is now Tsavo National Park but
in the late 1890's when the Uganda Railway was under
construction the work was seriously stalled for three
weeks at the Tsavo River as a result of two lions dragging off twenty-eight Indian railway workers, and an
unknown number of natives of the area. The railway
workers were terrified. By the end of 1898 many had
deserted.

The first few people killed and eaten by the lions
were of no consequence to the workers but when the
lions became more successful at dragging people out
of the camps the workers began attributing super-
natural powers to the pair which seemed to have such
an uncanny ability to escape traps and waiting rifle-
men.

One night two construction trains rammed each
other at Tsavo. Although it was against regulations,
many workers were riding the cars and several were
killed and injured. Survivors heard the lions growling
in the darkness and were terrified, but help arrived

before the lions reached those trapped in the wreckage.

The section engineer, Colonel J. H. Patterson, was an enthusiastic sportsman and spent practically all of his time trying to kill the pair. Poisoned animal carcasses left in the brush for the lions were ignored.

One government official was attacked soon after he left the train at Tsavo and walked toward Patterson's camp. A lion leaped onto the official and knocked him down but as he fell the official's rifle discharged, diverting the lion from the official, but the lamp-carrying native following him was dragged off into the brush.

Later the lions killed a donkey and left it. Patterson had a *machan*, or platform, built nearby and waited there the next night. One lion appeared but Patterson soon realized that it was not interested in the donkey. It was stalking him.

For two hours Patterson stared into the surrounding bushes as he turned with the circling lion. Finally the lion showed itself briefly and Patterson killed it with a single shot.

Still trying every trick known to lion hunting Patterson hunted the other man-eater. A goat was tied to a stake outside the camp. The lion killed it and dragged it into the brush leaving an adequate trail for Patterson to follow. He managed to wound the evasive lion which dropped from sight for a week and the camp fervently hoped that it had died.

Ten nights later, however, the lion tried to get to a

platform of sleeping railway workers. The following night Patterson waited on the platform, too. The lion returned and Patterson wounded him but the lion escaped into the brush.

Patterson was tenacious. At daylight he began his own stalk into the brush. The lion charged furiously several times and Patterson met each with rifle blasts. On the last charge the lion fell dead five yards from the persistent Patterson.

Other man-eating lions plagued the railway. Three months later in March, 1899, an engineer named O'Hara was dragged from his tent and killed. Lions harassed the track-laying workers at the head of the project so frequently that the workers had to be brought into protected camps at night.

The next June a man-eater began operations at Kima Station, sixty miles from Nairobi. One night it attempted to tear off the corrugated iron roofing sheets to get at the station attendant, and a few nights later it killed a native employee.

A locomotive engineer hid in an empty water tank one night with the intention of ambushing the lion. The lion came that night, overturned the empty tank and tried to reach the terrified man. The engineer finally remembered his rifle and fired it, scaring the lion away.

A superintendent of railway police determined to take this lion and had his railway car moved onto a siding here. Two friends, Hubner and Parenti, were to alternate watches with him. The superintendent took the first watch. Unfortunately, his day's travel had exhausted him and he soon fell asleep.

Hubner awakened shortly. Some instinct warned him not to move. The lion was in the railway car!

The door through which the lion entered had swung closed and the lock snapped shut. The lion was trapped inside, a fact which the lion seemed not to recognize. Instead he was at the superintendent's side when Hubner's eyes opened.

The latter saw the lion seize the superintendent. The man's outcry was stifled when the lion's paw hit the man's head and teeth gripped the man's chest. The lion dragged the body to the floor. Parenti was already on the floor where he had made his bed. Hubner did not know if he were dead or alive. The man was motionless.

Hubner decided he had better act while he had a chance. He dived over the lion's back to the door. Snapping the catch open he found that terrified servants were holding the door shut to keep the lion from getting out to them. While Hubner shouted frantically in his efforts to get the door open the lion picked up the superintendent's body and dived out the window.

The prostrate Parenti who had remained unhurt and quiet as the lion stood on him with hind feet now leaped to his feet in a state of shock. He jumped out the window the lion had used and sprinted for the station.

The lion was caught in a box trap shortly and exhibited for a few days before it was shot.

Farther south even more railroad workers were killed and eaten by lions. Thirty native Africans building the Beira, Mozambique-to-Salisbury tracks were dragged off by man-eaters in the Pungue Flats, thirty miles inland from the seacoast. These Africans, Shangaans, were not cowed by the man-eaters, however. They gathered up weapons and sent out hunting parties to stop the depredations.

There are significant numbers of Africans today who would like nothing better than to see every lion shot as soon as possible. Such views horrify non-African conservationists or preservationists, who want Africans to keep their wildlife populations intact regardless of the consequence to the people who must live in lion habitat.

The Africans who would like to wipe out the lion population are those whose families and villages have been dented by lions. Today's Africa is a far cry from the Africa David Livingstone explored. Paved roads, railroads, hundreds of airfields and all the other indications of modern life are found over most of the continent and many African cities are more modern than European cities of similar size. Yet Africa's lions live today much as they did during past centuries. Africans will be killed and eaten by lions this year and each year for the foreseeable future.

In 1958 and 1959 when Joy Adamson's famous lioness, Elsa, was a young adult, Joy's husband had to spend several weeks hunting two lions which had mauled or killed twenty-eight members of the Boran Tribe in northern Kenya. At night the lions forced themselves into the tribal bomas, or enclosures, and dragged screaming people away without interference from the terrified villagers. After the man-eaters were killed the Adamsons found that the two had left in the bush healthy cubs with a taste for humans. The cubs continued the terrorizing for a time until they were stopped.

What is it like to be dragged by a lion? It appears that the average victim experiences limited pain. Shock grips the victim quickly after the lion seizes the victim who is carried along loosely with lion teeth holding, rather than biting. The victim's skin may or may not be punctured during the dragging.

Dr. Bernhard Grzimek, who has observed the lion extensively in the Serengeti Plains as well as the Frankfurt Zoo, believes that animals held in a lion's mouth do not feel pain or fear. In fact, he has stated, "I could almost say I know it."

David Livingstone, the early African explorer, was once attacked by a lion. The lion shook him violently as a dog would a smaller animal, growling furiously as it did so. "The shock caused a stupor similar to that of a mouse caught by a cat," Livingstone said later. "It produced a sort of insensitivity during which I felt neither pain nor fear, although I was fully conscious.

I was like a patient under slight narcosis who watches an operation on himself but does not feel the scalpel. This singular condition was not due to a mental process but to shock which wiped out all feelings of fear and pain, even when viewing the lion directly." Other members of Livingstone's party drove off the lion and Livingstone recovered.

It is not an infrequent occurrence for a lion to place its prey on the ground momentarily and see it come to life and escape. Instinct seems to supplement shock as necessary to cause the prey to remain limp while it is held by the lion. One South African game ranger, Wolhuter, riding a horse through a dry river bed was seized during an attack by two lionesses. One sank her teeth into his right shoulder and dragged him ninety yards. The initial bite seemed to paralyze him and he felt no pain; however, as he skidded along beneath her belly he regained enough sense to pull his belt knife free with his left hand. When she laid him down he stabbed her in the chest twice. She backed away then in the face of the man's barking dogs and he managed to climb a tree and tie himself to a limb until rescued.

Perhaps the record for numbers of people eaten was made by an Uganda lion of the 1920's. It ate a known eighty-four. The immediate reason for such man-eating was a rinderpest epidemic which almost eradicated hoofed herds in Uganda's Ankole province bordering Queen Elizabeth National Park.

Lions in the area began taking domestic stock, then some of the herders. Shortly a rash of man-eaters developed when the lions found human flesh more to their liking than that of a goat or cow. The area around Sanga was especially afflicted by man-eating lions. Each night lions prowled the villages, pouncing on people and attempting to claw open doors. Some villages were deserted by terrified inhabitants.

The main road between the Congo, Rwanda and Lake Victoria became a gauntlet for migrant workers walking to Uganda looking for work, or returning home. Most of these workers slept in the open along the road and there is no way of ascertaining how many were dragged off by lions. The Sanga man-eaters spread as far as 100 miles away. One versatile lion found that following a herd of crop-raiding elephants brought good results. Villagers rushed out beating drums to scare the elephants and the lion pounced on one of the drummers.

Game wardens and hunters kept up hunting pressure until seventeen lions were killed. The man-eating stopped for a time. In 1937 a dozen more lions began taking people in Ankole and lion hunting was intensified for a year and a half before these man-eaters were eradicated. On several occasions since World War Two man-eating lions have reappeared in the same area.

C. A. W. Guggisberg, who wrote the definitive lion book *Simba, The Life of the Lion,* in 1961 reported that "not very long ago" a Nyasaland lion began ambushing natives emerging from their huts at dawn, killing fourteen in one month. The same technique was used in Mozambique during the early part of the century by lions which killed and ate twenty people monthly.

Mozambique has had unusual numbers of man-eaters, both in early and recent years. Southern Tanzania is also notorious for man-eating lions. Two lions killed twenty-three natives within sixty days in 1923 and 1924. One principal road was patrolled regularly by four pairs of lions earlier, each pair working its own section of the road to pounce on passing natives.

In 1953, the chief game warden of a Tanzanian province reported, "All the lions in this Province are liable to eat people if circumstances permit. . ." In July, 1960, a lioness killed and partially ate a cook on a northern Tanzanian farm. In 1958, a lion in central Tanzania lost several teeth when shot by a native's muzzle-loading weapon. Unable to kill regular prey he began killing porcupines and soon had quills in numerous parts of his body. Then he found how easy it was to kill men. He did this for the next twelve months although hunters stayed on his trail almost every day. One village of 300 people was deserted by its inhabitants who found a sanctuary far beyond the lion's range. Then on two consecutive days the lion killed two people at places close to each other. A game warden immediately took up the lion's trail, following it for two days over sixty miles before he killed it.

One trait of people who live close to danger successfully is an ability to see some humor in near-tragedy. One of these incidents repeated by Guggisberg is still told to a background of much laughter in Bechuanaland. It happened years ago. A native on his way home at dusk was attacked by a lion. The man dodged and barely managed to escape the lion's swipe by rushing up a tree. The lion studied the situation as he walked around below and apparently decided that the man would come down before long. The lion made himself comfortable and began his wait.

The man managed to stay awake most of the night. Just before dawn, however, he fell asleep and toppled from his limb. He landed with wildly waving arms and legs on top of the dozing lion.

The lion was on his feet before the man, and running. He was out of sight before the man reached the tree again.

The lion-vs-man situation at Tsavo and other stations may never be solved satisfactorily. Railway officials in Nairobi preserved a number of telegrams from "besieged" station masters. One August, 1905 predawn wire from Simba Station reported, ". . . Lion is on the platform . . . Guard is to advise passengers not to get out here. . ." Shortly after dawn a wire reported, "One African injured at 6 o'clock again by lion and hence sent to Makindu Hospital. . ." At four in the afternoon another wire stated, "Pointsman (switchman) is surrounded by two lions . . . Pointsman went on top of telegraph post near water tanks. Train to stop there and take him on train. . ."

An April, 1908 Tsavo telegram from the station master reported, ". . . Myself, shedman, porters all in office. Lion sitting before office door."

A 1955 Tsavo telegram said, "Urgent. Odeke narrowly escaped from being caught by lion . . . Closing for night working if no protection." Odeke was the assistant station master. When the train arrived he stepped to a station truck but was stopped by a growl. His flashlight beam showed a snarling lion a few steps away. The man escaped by leaping onto the train while another trainman blew his whistle. This unsettled the lion and it ran beneath the train and out the other side.

When C. A. W. Guggisberg and his wife visited Tsavo National Park soon after one camp in the Ngulia Hills was opened, they were warned emphatically by the game warden not to sleep outside their hut because of a man-eating lion in the vicinity. Two nights earlier it had seized a road worker at a nearby camp but was scared away before the man was seriously injured.

From 1960 to the first few days of 1965 a lion killed and ate a known eight persons near Darajani, a station less than forty miles from Tsavo Station. Game rangers had no success when they tried to track it down. On the night of January 5, 1965 the train from Mombasa pulled into the station, dropping off mail and slowing to take on water at the tower at the edge of the station grounds. The station master walked out and alongside the train toward the tower.

Just before the train reached it a lion jumped up from the grass near the tower and ran a few yards. Then he stopped and stared back at the train, his tail curling from side to side. The station master shouted to the locomotive engineer to get his water up the line, and sprinted for his office where he and his switchman locked themselves in for the night.

They heard the lion prowling outside several times during the night. At daylight they saw it, big but gaunt, waiting near the water tower. Then it stood and walked toward the station. Finally it turned away and walked down an access road leading to the Nairobi-Mombasa tarmac, or paved highway. Twenty minutes later the lion killed a Wakamba farmer who lived nearby and had just come out of his hut to chase elephants out of his cornfield.

Shortly the station master sent a wire to a game ranger thirty-five miles up the line. "Please arrange to come urgently . . . A lion has caught a man . . . and he is still eating him up to now."

Although game scouts were dispatched immediately, by coincidence a safari hunter, John Kingsley-Heath, and his client, American engineer John Perrot on leave from Libyan oil fields, turned into the Darajani access road shortly after the attack. Kingsley-Heath spotted the Wakamba's bow and arrows lying in the road near a pool of blood. Quick investigation showed that the lion had leaped from the grass only a few feet in front of the man and apparently killed him immediately.

The two followed the drag marks through tall grass toward a thick stand of brush about twenty by forty yards in dimension. They were stopped by a shattering roar. The lion charged, stopped while still out of sight, and returned to its victim.

Kingsley-Heath moved close enough to see the dead man with the lion's hindquarters resting on him. There was no chance of an accurate shot. Since he had been severely mauled by a Tanganyikan lion in earlier years resulting in both arms being broken, one foot crushed and a lacerated back, Kingsley-Heath was not inclined to repeat the experience with a wounded lion.

There was a tall tree growing at one end of the thicket. A fork twelve feet from the ground allowed observation of the entire thicket and surrounding grassland. A shooter here could take the man-eater regardless of where he emerged. Since the tree was ten yards inside the thicket the two had some ticklish moments working into the dense brush to the tree base. The lion growled occasionally but seemed more interested in getting food into its body.

Perrot climbed quietly into the tree and Kingsley-Heath backed out to organize the gathering natives. He would enter the other end of the thicket, show a white handkerchief and wait with rifle ready while they threw stones into the spot where the lion was eating.

Perrot put a shot through the lion's body as it rushed out. The lion saw Kingsley-Heath and his assistant at that moment and charged from twenty yards. Kingsley-Heath's first shot went through the lion's shoulder and tore his heart apart. The lion did not miss a step. Seizing a .458 caliber rifle from his assistant Kingsley-Heath put two bullets into the lion just as it left the ground in a final spring from six feet away. The lion fell at his feet, still kicking.

The lion's skull measured ten inches across, about as large as lion skulls get, and its teeth and claws were in their prime, indicating that the lion was not deteriorating with age. However, it weighed only 380 pounds when it should have weighed over 400.

A number of porcupine quills had imbedded themselves in the lion's chest and shoulder, but these had broken off and had been insulated by protective growths between skin and muscle so that they caused the lion little difficulty. However, one quill had been driven nine inches up the lion's left nostril. Over two inches protruded from the nostril. This quill undoubtedly generated much pain.

Despite this quill Kingsley-Heath believed the lion had taken to man-eating because of encroaching civilization in the area. Poaching, farming and drought had almost extinguished the lion's normal prey and caused it to take up man-hunting.

Why do healthy lions take up man-eating? It may happen, as it did in Uganda and in the recent Darajani case, when hoofed prey is severely diminished. One story about the Tsavo man-eaters states that these two lions began their depredations only after eating railway workers who had died of disease and were left unburied in the bush. This could be true but man-eating lions were generating terror in the Tsavo area long before railway construction began.

An unsuspected factor which apparently sparks man-eating by today's African lions is the beginning of the rainy season. When vegetation and grass suddenly grow thick from nourishing rains lions have difficulty catching antelope prey. Such species as impala habitually leap over grass masses during flight. The lion must plow through the thick grass which is often tall enough to hamper vision. Consequently, in certain areas lions find it impossible to catch normal prey. Then they begin waiting along paths to ambush people. They may rove into settled areas where encounters with unarmed and unsuspecting natives occur frequently.

One premise of experts has it that lions avoid people because they cannot tolerate offensive human scent. This belief will not stand up in the light of the well-documented history of man-eating lions. In reality lions usually avoid man as soon as they detect his scent since they associate the scent, and man, with danger. The lion may not know what form this danger takes but its mother or a preceding mother witnessed destruction by rifles, spears or other weapons in the hands of man. The nervousness and flight reaction triggered in the mother by man's proximity is passed on to her cubs.

C. T. Astley Maberly, after a lifetime of observing African wildlife, believes this is the only reason lions tend to avoid man. Since they associate man with danger, some wounded lions that have mauled or killed a man have left him without eating any part.

Once a lion tastes a man's flesh, however, it tends to become a man-eater immediately and goes looking for more of this easily-taken prey. Cubs eating human flesh brought to them by their mothers will probably become man-eaters.

People are not inclined to consider their senses on a par with wild animals. In the case of the lion, however, the animal's strong acrid scent can be easily smelled by the average person. This distinctive scent can often be detected on grass and brush rubbed against by a passing lion. Any zoo's lion house which has housed its occupants for some time has this lingering, distinctive odor, sometimes so strong that visitors hurry out.

Modern travelers don't realize that Africa's lions today are potentially more dangerous to man than a few decades ago when the lion was considered vermin and shot on sight. Lions avoided man then except under unusual circumstances. Today, however, because of the increasing numbers of travelers through lion habitat, the lion views the camera-carrying man casually. People accustomed to seeing circus or zoo lions mixing harmlessly with trainers may assume wild lions are of a similar disposition and find themselves in trouble. This viewpoint is sometimes reinforced by great white hunters, safari guides, whose lion observations have been limited to lions avoiding rifle fire. These people speak with a knowing air of what the lion will do at the approach of man.

However, lions are no different from all other animals with some intelligence according to C. T. Astley Maberly. Their temperaments are subject to individuality. Most of them are high-strung and show fast-changing moods. A man walking in the grass usually causes lions to flee. Occasional men, no longer with us, have surprised lions who did not bolt.

It is unbelievable to see how well sparse, knee-high grass can conceal lions. A lion's coat has none of the disruptive patterns and camouflaging spots of the leopard and cheetah, yet its pelage melts into the grass and brush of its chosen habitat. I photographed a pride of eight lions in Kenya's Masai Mara Reserve lying in afternoon shade with no attempt at concealment. Two were stretched out across an old vehicle path that ran through grass. Although I thought I counted eight at the time, my photographs from thirty steps away show only three. If I had been walking I would have found myself among these lions before I spotted the first one.

So persuasive has been the cry for conservation of

African animals, most of us have come to visualize the Africa of free-ranging lions and other large animals as a thing of the past. However, the hazards of wandering afoot at night in many areas have not diminished. Instead, they have increased substantially over the past few years where game reserves have allowed animal populations to expand rapidly.

In 1965, two thieves rifled the cash from Tanzania's Mikumi Game Lodge bar one night and started walking along the main road toward their village. They were soon confronted by a pride of lions, and managed to hitchhike on a truck returning to the lodge. The truck driver reported the pair's suspiciously late hike to the police who soon arrested them.

During 1965 a train headed out from the seacoast along Tanzania's cross-country railway braked violently one night in an effort to avoid hitting lions lying across the track. One car was derailed in the process and one lion was killed. The rest of the pride stalked around their dead companion growling their anger and preventing repairs. The train was delayed six hours.

It is easy for us to be brave in the presence of wild animals when we are unaware of the threat offered by them. Unfortunately most people receive their store of wildlife knowledge from a visit to the circus or the zoo where lions and bears look like big, stupid clowns jumping at the commands of a man's voice or begging for peanuts with outstretched paws. Nine out of ten visitors to Yellowstone and the Great Smoky Mountain National Parks fall into this category. They ignore the warnings against feeding the bears. Each year dozens of these visitors are injured by wild bears whose response to the scent of food is to take it. If it is in a pocket, the pocket is ripped off. If it is in a closed fist, the fist may be shattered by a fast bear paw swipe.

The point of this aside is to emphasize the importance of reading several sources, never only one or two, about wildlife and their habitat before a visit. Because a trip to Africa was no ordinary thing for us, it was only natural that we devoured everything we could get our hands on about Africa's wildlife before we had the chance to see it. One lasting impression of this study was a healthy respect for elephants and lions, especially the latter. Inside a vehicle visitors are safe at almost any distance from a lion, but outside a vehicle or compound in big game country a man is an intruder in another's habitat.

Consequently, we watched with some awe the unforgettable day and night experienced by a London travel agent in Ngorongoro Crater. The crater, about twelve miles across, contains the world's highest concentration of big game including many of the magnificent big, black-maned lions so prized by trophy hunters.

The agent, a likable, young businessman whose demeanor was shy at most, was a pale product of years under London's overcast. He blushed when he talked if there were several listeners and his conversations soon revealed that a city sidewalk was the only habitat he knew. His employing travel agency sent him down for a three-day stay in East Africa so he could better advise clients.

All went well for him initially. His lack of preparation for the sudden trip allowed all of us in our photographic safari to help him with small favors: a toothbrush, razor, soap sufficient for him to get along.

One hitch in his visit shortly became apparent. His employer apparently lost him. Every arrangement for a pick-up by plane or vehicle along our route failed to materialize. He was delighted with the prolonged vacation.

Finally firm arrangements were made. A plane coming down to Ngorongoro from Nairobi was scheduled to pick him up one morning. He was taken to the strip early by a game-viewing vehicle. After waiting a short time he insisted that the game viewers continue their day's schedule and he stepped out to await the plane.

Ngorongoro's strip is like most African airstrips, a stretch of relatively flat ground with practically no improvements except flattened anthills. The bareheaded young man from London soon found that the big game population failed to take notice of man's airstrip. The herds of zebra and wildebeest wandered past, parting to avoid brushing against this diminutive human standing in the open a half mile from the nearest tree.

Our friend viewed this situation with some misgiving. There are several dozen black rhinos in Ngorongoro. Black rhinos are notoriously short-tempered. None came close as far as our friend could tell. The equatorial sun grew hotter and generated heat reflections off the crater floor which played subtle tricks on his vision.

With some apprehension he saw distant hyenas watching him. From time to time he stared at lions waiting at the edge of a papyrus marsh. He grew more apprehensive. There were no other humans within sight. He had no weapons. There were no burrows in which he might seek refuge in case of emergency, let alone any trees within reach.

He spent the day there without food or water. He had no illusions about the dominance of man over wildlife assumed by so many people. A dozen times he wondered what he would do if a lion stalked over to the edge of the airstrip to examine this obviously defenseless human.

Night came. The lions began their roaring. Zebras barked in alarm. Wild dog packs chittered their odd rustling bark as they began hunting. Hyenas ran their unnerving laughter up and down the scale.

Our friend spent a night he will never forget. Forms materialized from the darkness and faded away again. He knew the danger of lying down out here by himself so he spent a sleepless night on his feet.

We saw him the next morning. A game crew spotted

him, brought him out of the crater and intercepted our vehicle on the rim road. He was blistered red, thirsty, and hungry. He may have had a few gray hairs he did not have before. Perhaps it was just as well that he had had little opportunity to study African animals in detail before his trip.

What are the chances of a visitor to Africa's game reserves being dragged from his tent at night? They are practically nil. If a person sleeps alone in the open he invites trouble from a variety of sources: insects, snakes and possibly a hungry lion. A person sleeping in the open in most of America, however, is more likely to be bitten by more insects, and has a better chance of meeting a poisonous snake than in Africa's lion country.

America's big game does far more damage to the casual camper than Africa's lions do to campers there. My home is in Santa Fe, New Mexico. During each of the past two summers campers sleeping in bedrolls less than ten miles from the state capitol building have been slapped by unprovoked, passing black bears severely enough to require hospital treatment and New Mexico has relatively few bears. Yellowstone National Park is notorious for bear attacks, most apparently caused by ignorant visitors feeding bears in violation of numerous warning signs. From 1931 to 1964, 936 Yellowstone bears had to be killed by rangers as a control measure. During this period 1,609 injuries by bears were reported to Park officials and one official estimated that twice that number went unreported. Four people have been killed by Yellowstone bears in the past fifty years.

Are we suggesting that it may be more dangerous to take unnecessary chances with big game in American parks than in African parks? Yes, we are.

6: *Wild Freedom?*

ONE OF THE ENDURING BELIEFS OF MAN IS THAT "FREE-
dom" means to animals what it does to man. Perhaps
no picture as painted in animal books and films is as
warming as that of the lion, mustang or wolf roaming
free and uninfluenced by man. It is a pleasing picture
from which all of us derive satisfaction.

Unfortunately almost no animal enjoys the freedom
we picture for it. In Africa, the constant thinning and
increase of animal populations affect prey and predator alike. Misery comes with cold soaking rains and
parching dry seasons which cause frantic elephants
to rip apart giant baobab trees and chew moist fibers.
Every tree line, brush clump, and papyrus patch in
marshland, harbor the threat of a lurking predator. In
the open, danger can materialize at any moment on
racing legs, on silent wings dropping from the sky,
or from an unseen wire snare. The few dominant animals: elephants, lions, rhinos, have little to fear from
large predators, but have no defense against tiny parasites and diseases which can reduce them to walking
shadows before early death.

In 1962, in Tanzania's Ngorongoro Crater, a 100-

square-mile basin of rich grassland, hordes of biting flies matured after unusually long rains. Lions were driven almost to distraction. One pride of six was found forty feet up in acacia trees where they sought relief from the flies, *Stomaxys calcitrans*. Others shoved into hyena holes in futile attempts to escape the bites. Photographs of lions huddled on tree limbs showed skins spotted with large wounds caused by scratching and resulting infections. This was "freedom" from man's viewpoint since Ngorongoro is a conservation area protected from hunting. Within weeks the crater's lion population dropped from sixty to fifteen. Three years later the lion population had regained only half its former number.

Gerald Durrell, animal collector and zoologist, told in his book *The Bafut Beagles* of the many visitors to his camp in the Cameroons of West Africa. An ever-popular animal group was the baby monkey section. One young lady, torn by the pathetic expressions on the monkey faces, berated him at length for his cruelty in depriving the young monkeys of their mothers and the "joys of freedom" in the jungle where they had a "carefree, happy existence."

The straight-faced Durrell asked her if she wanted to assist him in a physical check-up of a baby monkey brought in by a native hunter a few hours before. The animal-lover agreed immediately.

She expressed surprise when Durrell said that the physical examination was actually a search for parasites. She remarked that she did not realize monkeys had parasites.

Durrell started his task by spreading the monkey's excretia over a sheet of paper. There were numbers of tiny worms in it. The young woman stared hard but said nothing.

Then Durrell examined the monkey, looking for swollen toes and fingers. He found six jigger fleas, *Hectopsyllidae*, under nails. The female of this parasite burrows beneath nails or into other tender skin where she feeds off the blood of her host while eggs mature. During this period she swells in size and causes acute pain to the unfortunate host. If her body is broken in an attempt to dislodge her, decay often results and toes or fingers are lost.

Durrell froze the affected toes and fingers with a local anesthetic and removed the fleas with a needle. The young woman grew pale.

This done Durrell found two lumps on the monkey's tail. These were filled with the larvae of a forest fly, one of the metallic blow flies, which deposit eggs in living animals. By the time Durrell removed these repulsive grubs the young woman hurried away to the other side of the clearing. She did not visit the camp again.

"I always think it rather a pity," said Durrell, "that people don't learn more about the drawbacks of life in the jungle before prating about the cruelty of captivity."

Even in the remotest wilderness or plains where some animals never see a man no animal is free to range wherever it wishes. Almost all are restricted to well-defined territories or neighborhoods. Strangely, the widest-ranging animal life such as elephants or birds adapt most easily to zoo life and live longer there than in the wild. Zoologists are still puzzled about why birds usually live better in small cages than large aviaries.

What may seem a vast territory to a man's casual glance shrinks drastically upon investigation. Lions in South Africa's Kruger Park were found to remain in ranges averaging slightly larger than three by four miles. Only a small part of this area was ever visited since prey was taken in selected areas. America's Ernest Thompson Seton reminded us sixty years ago that "No wild animal roams at random over the country." They follow the same routes and trails, often with such regularity that all grass is worn away by their passing.

At first glance we assume that a wild animal's territory, aside from dictates of reproduction and family life, has a need for sufficient elbow room for plenty of exercise. We visualize lions, zebras, and wildebeests rushing about stretching legs and muscles and thundering over distant ridges. Actually the need for activity has little to do with the size of an animal's territory. Food defines it.

A lush grassland, such as Ngorongoro Crater with

its year-round springs, supports a heavy animal population. At times there has been almost one lion to each square mile. In such a habitat a pride of lions may never move more than a few hundred yards away from their favorite resting spot. Lions have bred and remained in good health in the cages of traveling circuses in Europe. In a zoo the average lion seems almost content to have only enough space to eat and stretch out for a long nap. The important thing, it appears, is ample food. A large exercise yard is fine but of limited value.

By the way, what made Joy Adamson's wonderful lion books so popular? The easy answer suggests that it is because of an almost universal love for cuddly lion cubs. I do not believe this is the real answer. Very few women would tolerate a lion cub in their house for even a short time. The real Joy Adamson, who may very well be the most envied single woman alive today, is admired by girls, married women and spinsters alike for her stimulating life in an environment which is all that we ever imagined Tarzan's to be. *Born Free, Living Free* and *Forever Free* use that irresistible catch word "free" which sweeps all of us before it, even if it has infinite meanings. The freedom-from-interference definition which most of us use for the word has little application to Elsa the lioness or her cubs. It applies to Joy herself, her life in Africa's most beautiful country of clear blue skies, of reading and writing under a tree by an African river, of frequent dependence on her own two hands and intellect to do things unknown to city apartment dwellers who lost so much of their own freedom in exchange for comfort and convenience.

Few of us are aware that many of the frontier conditions we associate with earlier times are still found almost everywhere. The change from frontier to modern cities and industrial complexes has occurred in an incredibly short time in the viewpoint of Europeans whose cities were already old before Columbus was born. In East Africa these same changes have occurred twice as fast.

In 1900, Nairobi, Kenya did not exist. It began with a tent village of railroad men and a few venturesome farmers set up on the Athi Plains by a river called Nairobi by the Masai. As the village grew rapidly, lions occasionally chased zebra and wildebeest through the streets as late as the 1930's. Now Nairobi is rapidly approaching a half-million population, yet lions still roam freely to the city's boundary. Fences keep the lions and other large animals out of town and off the runways of Wilson Airport and encourage them to come no farther than the Nairobi National Park.

However, one problem of frontier cattlemen of sixty years ago still has not been solved satisfactorily. The dairy herds which graze near here are still subject to lion raids at night. Most lions tend to ignore cattle herds when wild herds are plentiful, but once beef is captured and tasted a lion acquires a taste for it.

In 1964, three lion prides pushed under the loose fence and strolled over Douglas Watson's Villa Franca dairy farm and killed some of his cattle. One of the Watson brothers retaliated by shooting some of the lions among his cows. Conservationists produced a "national outcry." This outcry did little, however, to correct the loss suffered by the dairy herd. In 1967, despite all the precautions taken by the Watsons, lions killed another seven dairy cattle. Meanwhile, life for the Watsons on the plains within sight of Nairobi's tall buildings still has many of the basic ingredients of the frontier's battle of wits between man and animal.

In parts of Africa abnormally affected by drought, lions often find it so easy to take weakened antelope during early drought periods that they lose their appetites for day-old meat. They may eat only fresh meat and their depredations added to the severe effects of drought destroy the hoofed herds at a rate that goes beyond scavengers' ability to remove the carrion. One ranger in southern Africa estimated that the 100 lions using the drought-stricken area he patrolled, about fifty square miles, took a kill every four or five days, or about 600 hoofed animals per month.

When river beds in Africa's lion country are dry, elephants save thousands of animals from dying of thirst by digging shallow wells in the river sand. After they drink and move on other species troop down to the precious water. Lions, however, may or may not use these muddied wells. Some lions prefer to scoop out their own wells, digging with front paws in the manner of dogs.

Lions dislike prolonged sun and heat. They seek shade at every opportunity and spend little time in the open except on overcast days or at night. Lions are not considered tree-climbing cats but in many parts of its habitat in East Africa low acacia limbs make it easy for them to escape flies and heat and sprawl over limbs. On occasion lions have climbed into trees and stolen leopard caches. One of my favorite photographs is of three young lions resting near Seronera on the Serengeti Plains. They have aligned themselves carefully in the shade of a narrow tree which is no larger than a power line pole. Only a single paw protrudes from the shaded strip.

Actually many parts of the United States, the Eastern Seaboard and the South, would make a poor habitat for the lion (assuming reserves and suitable prey were available) because they are too hot. Almost all of African lion country gets chilly to cold at night because of relatively high altitudes. Anytime the temperature gets above eighty degrees the lion hunts cool shadows. Consequently the lion normally confines hunting and other physical activity to the cooler parts of the day, dawn, dusk and night.

The lion's territory can be surprisingly small. My introduction to East Africa's game reserves was the Masai Mara Reserve in western Kenya. We flew out of Nairobi across the Rift Valley and into the *keekorok,* or brushy hill country, which makes up much of this reserve. Our pilot, June Sutherland, was a married woman of middle age and rated one of Africa's best bush pilots by the owner of the flying service which had employed her for years. She flew past the long dirt runway at altitude. There was a herd of several hundred wildebeests standing on one end of the runway and I waited for her to dip down and scare them away with a low pass. Instead she dipped a wing into a forward slip and eased onto the cleared portion of the runway so skillfully that I could not detect the contact of tires to ground until we were taxiing at speed.

We rolled past three African buffalo grazing near the lodge and stopped a short distance from the entrance. The Keekorok Lodge has some of the aspects of an American motel but enough of the atmosphere of a defended camp to remind one that this part of Africa belongs to wildlife, not man. Armed guards spent the night before a bonfire in the center of the lawn. The back of the lodge units formed a wall designed to stop wildlife intrusions. Open spaces in this protective wall contained signs warning visitors not to step beyond.

Periodically during the first night there, alarmed zebras barked and stampeded to safer grounds. Their voices are literal barks, not unlike a coyote's and none of the zebras seemed far away.

The next morning we began a game-viewing drive

in roll-top Volkswagen buses, a better photographic platform than the four-wheel-drive Land Rover. We had gone less than 200 yards when our driver eased to a stop and pointed to a zebra lying under a bush. Its glazed eyes showed that it had been dead for hours. Behind it rested a lion already stuffed and not yet interested in further eating. Beyond him were two lionesses and several grown cubs. They were disinterested in eating at the moment.

It took a while for me to realize the detachment with which these lions viewed the activities at Keekorok Lodge, and to comprehend the paradox between virtually all modern improvements one would find in a New York City hotel there, and the primeval way of life still followed by animals a few yards away.

So plentiful are the wildebeests, zebras, Thomson's gazelles, impala and topi antelope within sight of the lodge that the territories claimed by lion prides there are very small. We saw two prides of six to eight individuals within 400 yards of each other, both less than 800 yards from the lodge.

Although most Tarzan films show lions roaming freely in the jungle this is not the case. About the only good reasons for having lions in jungle films is because there are plenty of trained lions available, and because Africa and lions are synonymous to most of us. However, jungle country is not lion country.

Ivan Sanderson, veteran naturalist and animal collector, once stepped around a huge tree root in a central African jungle and found himself face to face with a lion. They eyed each other momentarily then headed in opposite directions at full speed. The lion had wandered into the jungle by accident when it followed a strip of savanna into the forested area. It had managed to penetrate eighty miles at least to the point where Sanderson met it. None of Sanderson's associates believed his story until he took them to the spot and showed them the tracks.

With the exception of buffalo, the lion is seldom inclined to invite trouble from large dangerous animals such as elephants and rhinos. Nor is the lion apt to invite encounters with man in areas open to hunting. Despite these two sources of trouble to a secure life the lion is by no means free from the host of hazards which afflict other species. Cubs die when long treks have to be made to find food. They are killed occasionally by predators when mothers leave them momentarily. Adults fight over food, territory, and while courting. They are gored by belligerent prey or cut by thorns and broken twigs. These wounds may develop into crippling infections. These injured lions eventually drop out of the pride, as well as old lions which cannot keep pace. Hyenas often drag such lions down and eat them.

Ticks are a nuisance, and often a fatal nuisance, to lions and most other animals in Africa or America. Joy Adamson's lioness Elsa died of a disease known as *Babesia* transmitted by a tick.

In short the wilderness life is no bed of roses even for the king of beasts. While we're on the subject of ticks, I have wondered for years why otherwise knowledgeable people such as African hunters, scientists, researchers and safari guides insist on wearing shorts. No one with any awareness of the trouble he invites is inclined to leave legs bare even for walking on trails, yet films of African hunts show shorts-clad safari guides rushing off through elephant grass. Some of these men have lived in Africa all their lives.

Bare skin invites insect bites in Africa or America. Ticks in particular are thick in areas of high game populations. Africa has its share of deadly snakes: cobras, mambas, boomslangs, puff adders, and Gaboon vipers, etc., which can kill a man with less than a well-aimed strike. One reading of the pain endured by the victim of a snake bite is enough to make one discard shorts and reach for long trousers and boots. Even the thinnest trousers provide some protection from a snake strike and may even absorb the impact before fangs reach the skin.

But don't Africans know best what should be worn in their own outdoors? The answer can be provided by another question. Don't Americans know best what should be worn when they fish and hunt in areas with high snake populations? No, they do not. Most people wear what is most comfortable or what is considered in fashion at the moment. On today's big game safaris and photo trips Africans and outsiders alike buy "safari outfits" consisting of a more-or-less practical bush jacket and matching short pants because these items are found in the best men's stores of Nairobi, Johannesburg and other African cities.

But what about black Africans in their tribal villages? Why don't they wear long trousers and boots? Most would if they had them. Those who do have them save these items for important occasions, such as market days and for dress-up. They would rather risk a snake bite than tear prized trousers on a snag.

A hot climate is not a real reason for wearing shorts. The hottest temperature recorded by a meteorological unit was in Libya in 1922. This was 136 degrees. Shorts are rare in Libya. The most common garments, Arabian or European, cover maximum skin for protection.

What should one wear in African jungles and grasslands? Any clothing which provides a barrier to insects, thorns and the rare prospect of a snake bite, such as long, loose trousers tucked into boots. Tight trousers with a stretched or taut surface can absorb little impact from a snake's strike although they can provide insect protection.

Is the wilderness lion, hunted by men, bitten by snakes and insects, wracked with disease at times, injured by other lions and stubborn prey, in any danger of extinction? No, nothing on the horizon suggests particular danger to the lion whose social way of life gives it a better chance of survival than such solitary cats as the cheetah. In today's Africa as in most of Africa's past periods lion numbers fluctuate largely according to the fluctuations of prey herds, which change principally according to rainfall and epidemics.

Today's African lion lives in an artificially protected environment. The world's most efficient predator, man, has been barred from taking lions in vast areas with the consequence that lion populations are generally stable.

Today lions are plentiful in Rhodesia, Mozambique (Portuguese East Africa), Southwest Africa, most of East Africa (Kenya, Tanzania and Uganda) and protected areas of such highly-developed countries as South Africa. There are even scattered reports of lions returning to areas which have not seen them for decades. The over-all range of the lion in Africa has not diminished significantly except for the northern Mediterranean Coast where it was once found from Morocco to Tunisia, and in South Africa's lower portions. Elsewhere the lion can still be found in almost as many areas as it ever was but in lesser numbers because of urbanization, farming and man's activities which have pushed the lion into remoter areas.

7: *The Leopard, Friend or Foe?*

I ONCE WATCHED A SERENGETI GIRAFFE BOUNCE A LEOP-
ard for a suspenseful moment without the slightest
caution for the leopard's explosive temper. We were
driving along a scattered tree line at sunset when I
saw a giraffe feeding on a high limb. We stopped with
the sun behind the tree to get the best photographic
effect.

The drama was more than I had anticipated. When
I began shooting pictures I saw only the feeding
giraffe, each jerk of foliage bouncing the limb from
which it fed. After another exposure or so I became
aware of a leopard lying on the jiggling limb no more
than six feet from the giraffe's head. The leopard apparently was not hungry and had little interest in the
giraffe. Its main concern was to stay on the limb.

Then the giraffe's calf moved into the viewfinder.
The leopard's eyes turned to the calf. The mother
giraffe discovered the leopard, whirled, and headed
for safer ground with the calf at her heels.

Can the leopard, seldom exceeding 135 pounds,
kill a giraffe weighing close to one ton? I don't know.
I have found no record of such a kill. Photos do exist,

however, of giraffe parts cached in limbs and guarded by a leopard. In all probability a portion of a giraffe carcass was taken by the leopard after lions had had their fill and abandoned the kill temporarily. There is no doubt that it is possible for a leopard to kill a giraffe, perhaps more easily than lions could, if a leopard dropped onto the vulnerable head and blinded the giraffe.

The size of animals carried by leopards into trees is surprising. Alexander Lake watched a leopard weighing 100 pounds drag a 240-pound antelope for several hundred yards before pulling it into a tree and hanging it by the neck from a limb crotch.

The leopard, *Panthera pardus pardus*, exhibits more cunning, alertness and tenacity than the lion. Once engaged in a fight the leopard normally fights until one of the participants is dead. In contrast, the lion breaks off a fight and flees as soon as it finds the fight going against it. Even after a leopard's opponent is dead the spotted cat's fury seldom subsides until it disembowels the carcass.

The leopard generally kills larger hoofed animals in the same way as a lion, by leaping to the back and seizing the back of the neck while a forepaw grabs the face or muzzle and whips it back. The resulting fall often breaks the prey's neck.

Leopards rarely drop from overhanging limbs or rock unless this presents the only practical way to ambush prey. Most attacks against smaller antelope

Leopard

and other animals are made by stalking as close to the prey as possible, then charging with enough momentum to throw the prey on initial contact. Once the prey is down the leopard usually tries to get a throat grip to finish the kill.

Game biologist Richard Estes maintained a research camp in a strip of trees along a stream extending from Ngorongoro's lake. During two months in 1964 he found that a grown female leopard visited the area nightly and selected Estes' observation platform as her own observation and resting site. The platform was in a tree close enough to throw shade on Estes' cabin.

Estes would look her over frequently with his flashlight. The leopard was not disturbed by this. He found that her hunting did not include leaps from the platform onto prey below even though she had frequent opportunities to do this. Instead she stalked along the streambank brush and tall grass while she looked for potential victims.

Among the other prey she took were two Grant's gazelles weighing about 160 pounds each. These were apparently too heavy for her and she left them beside Estes' vehicle. She returned to them periodically to eat. Her chief prey, however, was the jackal. She caught eleven in a three-week period and carried them up to the platform. Those which remained alive were toyed with like a cat playing with a mouse until she tired of the game and killed them with a final bite.

Like both wild animals and man, the leopard is

inclined to take the easiest route to prey. The small
antelope or other animal most available is the principal
prey species. A leopard marooned on an island of the
rising Zambezi behind Kariba Dam ignored plentiful
baboons to take the little duiker antelopes which were
easy to catch and offered no resistance.

Almost every living form of life in the leopard's
habitat has been used by it for food. These include
men, dogs, baboons, fish, crabs, snakes, crocodiles,
ostriches, rats, eggs, wild fruit, cane rats, scorched
carcasses left by grass fires, parrots, domestic stock,
and a host of others. The leopard eats carrion in ad-
vanced stages of putrefaction.

Africans, as well as Americans, have learned through
experience the value of predators in keeping down
the animal hordes which eat crops or vital grass. The
coyote proved to be an irreplaceable foundation for
successful cattle raising in most of western America.
At first cattlemen shot the coyote on sight because it
occasionally killed calves. However, when the coyote
population dipped jack rabbits, prairie dogs and rats
increased their populations rapidly and whole ranges
were nibbled bare of grass. Cattlemen found that it
required ten or twenty times more rangeland to raise
a steer. Then the coyote received some protection. The
rodent population went down under coyote predation
and ranges produced ample grass crops again. Cattle
had adequate food, and ranch profits returned.

The leopard is a similar vital link in much of Africa

because it kills baboons. The baboon is so versatile that it can thrive under man's persecution and decimate his crops, especially grass which is the baboon's principal food. The baboon has learned to avoid man's poisons, snares, and rifles, but it is unable to cope effectively with the leopard. Frequently, baboons kill leopards, but for each leopard killed hundreds of baboons are killed by leopards. Another crop-destroyer population kept within bounds by the leopard is that of the rock hyrax, or rock rabbit, an animal resembling the American woodchuck.

More baboons are killed by leopards than by any other predator including man. Although universally despised by farmers the baboon can match wits with man because this highly gregarious animal lives in a troop which is well organized for defense, as well as for depredations on crops or wildlife. The leopard is successful in its baboon hunts only when it surprises lone individuals. No leopard in its right mind will stand up to a line of advancing baboons.

The damage baboons can do to such animals is unbelievable. The technique seldom varies. The baboon seizes the animal with its hands and feet, draws it close enough to sink teeth into its enemy, then shoves it away, the action ripping out a chunk of meat.

Baboons commonly exhibit surprising cooperation and accept a high degree of responsibility toward each other. Norman Carr watched a leopard scatter a baboon troop into sourrounding trees. There the baboons set up an angry outcry. One young baboon had been forgotten on the ground and set up a frightened squealing. An adult female, not its mother, scurried to the ground and retrieved the youngster at considerable danger to herself. She escaped into the limbs ahead of the leopard.

The leopard is the only predator with a special interest in wild canines. Lions and other predators kill jackals, African hunting dogs and feral dogs only infrequently, and may or may not eat them. Leopards, however, choose these members of the dog family in preference to other pray.

Wild running, or feral, domestic dogs are as much a problem in Africa as they are in America. Most feral packs are formed of dogs abandoned by poachers and even city dog owners, and these quickly become vicious upon their return to the wild. They are destructive to antelope calves as well as to the adults, and carry out bloody, if not successful, attacks on cattle and goats over most of Africa.

Leopards make daring forays to get their choicest morsel, the domestic dog, racing into camps, onto porches and even leaping through house windows to seize a dog. Usually the leopard is gone before any retaliatory action can be taken. Such attacks are so common that they are well known and expected throughout the leopard's range.

Naturalists would like to know more about the leopard populations than they do. It is indisputable that leopards are no longer plentiful in areas where they once thrived, though many naturalists believe that reports of declining leopard numbers in some areas are due to the animal's growing secretiveness. It is the only large African cat which can adapt readily to a changing environment and survive, even thrive, in a minimum amount of cover. The more the leopard is persecuted the more wary it becomes and the less often it is seen. It is not particularly disturbed by distant views of man, nor his houses. In fact, the leopard prowls villages with relative impunity, looking for dogs and even poultry.

Naturalists dispute the purpose of growls, screams or caterwauls in the cat family. It appears that these noises are suited to the situation. Many believe that a lion's growl or an American bobcat's caterwaul in thick vegetation serves frequently to flush prey into running and revealing locations. The leopard has a quiet growl, so low as to be deliberate, that seems intended to paralyze prey immediately before the charge. If so, and Peter Turnbull-Kemp who authored *The Leopard*, believes from personal observation that it is, then it is a noise to intimidate the opponent like a soldier's battle cry during a bayonet charge.

The leopard's most distinctive call has to be heard to be believed. It is not an ordinary growl nor the reverberating roar common to lions but a coarse rasping sound similar to an amplified sawing by a novice using a crosscut saw. The call is not restricted to one purpose such as mating, but is given in many situations: warning off competitors, frustration, anticipating a drink, satisfaction after drinking or downing prey, or maintaining contact with a distant animal. The leopard goes to much physical effort to produce it, lowering its head and showing obvious muscular strain while calling. It seems to be used on occasion to frighten baboons or other potential prey into revealing their locations. A recording issued in Nairobi by the Sapra Studio contains a segment of "conversation" between a leopard and baboons. A dog baboon barks in alarm after the leopard's coarse sawing call is heard and as the leopard continues the baboon troop barks and jabbers in excitement.

Although an occasional leopard may be caught up in the excitement of killing, especially in an enclosed area such as a stock pen where one leopard killed eighty goats one night, the average leopard is believed to kill only about twenty animals annually. If the kills are large antelopes and the leopard is not robbed of its prey by scavengers, the leopard may kill no more than twelve to fifteen annually.

Although highly respected by the well-armed hunter and feared by the unarmed native the leopard's chief enemy is man. It has no real defense against the clever hunter except secretiveness but when hard pressed it will not hesitate to attack an armed man.

Best known of these incidents to American readers was the desperate fight of Carl Akeley, one of the first to make the world aware of the need for conserving African wildlife. He wounded a leopard and was shortly attacked from ambush. Although Akeley weighed considerably more than the young leopard he had difficulty holding it down with one knee while he choked it to death.

The attack of a wounded leopard on Frank Miller, a partner in a Tanzanian safari outfit, a few years ago is probably typical of what any hunter can expect under the circumstances. Kermit Roosevelt, grandson of Theodore Roosevelt, described it in *Outdoor Life.* Miller's associate white hunter and his client had wounded a leopard. Returning to camp they asked Miller to come along with his shotgun to finish the job.

As they closed on the leopard, Miller's associate asked for the shotgun and Miller gave it to him. Miller continued the stalk unarmed and slightly ahead of armed companions to either side. The leopard leaped for Miller and sank his teeth into his scalp. Miller threw his arms around the leopard's middle, drawing it tight against him and forcing all four feet past his body so claws could do no damage. In the melee, which ended when Miller's client shot the leopard off him, Miller's scalp was ripped half off. Fortunately his client was a surgeon and did an expert job of sewing it back in place. Ten years later the rugged Miller was still leading safaris which included such well-known clients as Kermit Roosevelt.

The leopard's most formidable local enemy in its

habitat is the lion which occasionally robs the leopard of its prey even after the prey has been cached in a tree. A lion pride will ring the tree and intimidate the leopard into fleeing. Then one lion climbs the tree and dislodges the prey. The jealous lion tolerates no feline competition in its territory. Numerous reports exist of lions chasing a leopard into trees, or killing it if it was not fast enough. If the leopard is killed it is usually eaten by the lions.

Baboons may kill more leopards in areas of high baboon populations than other animals. African hunting dogs sometimes chase leopards from kills if the leopard does not get the carcass into a tree immediately. Despite its fighting ability the leopard occasionally is killed by such wildlife as crocodiles, pythons, hyenas, domestic dog packs, bush pigs and wart hogs. Numerous internal and external parasites affect it. Thirty species of ticks have been taken from leopards. Rabies and a virus infection popularly called cat flu take a toll.

The leopard is particularly susceptible to snake bite or a charge of venom from a spitting cobra because of its soft-footed movement. The snake does not receive warning vibrations in time to move out of the way and strikes in defense when the leopard suddenly appears before it.

This is most apt to happen at night when the leopard does most of its hunting. It has keen night vision as well as hearing, but its scent is not on par with some other animals in its habitat. Like many chiefly nocturnal animals the leopard also hunts on overcast days. It does not confine itself to these preferred hours but can be seen by accident at any hour.

Its territory is about the size of a lion's, up to a hundred square miles. In unusual circumstances it may be larger. One man-eating leopard covered 500 square miles.

Some of Africa's man-eating leopards established records which human populations of the area would sooner forget. In 1936 and 1937, one leopard killed a known sixty-seven people in the Chambesi. In 1938, a leopard killed eight people in Zambia's Luangwa Valley. In 1940, a leopard in the same area killed fifteen people with a bite to the throat, then abandoned the kill without eating any part of it.

Perhaps no man-eating animal becomes as wary as does the man-eating leopard. The leopard can be hunted or trapped with relative ease until it kills and eats a man. Then it seems to sense that it is matching wits with a new adversary possessing unusual skills and weapons. Consequently, it assumes an alertness it never marshaled before. Because of the difficulty of hunting a man-eating leopard successfully it is apt to accumulate an astonishing total of human victims before it is stopped.

A Madras, India newspaper of May, 1962 reported that 350 people had been killed in the area by man-eating leopards during the previous three years. Colonel Jim Corbett, who spent so many years hunting Indian man-eaters, reported 125 people killed by leopards in one area between 1918 and 1926.

The fact that leopards relish dogs above almost any food and will take high risks to obtain them may be indirectly responsible for some man-eating leopards developing their taste for humans. Dogs are found in villages or around campfires where there are usually people. A leopard waiting in the grass near a village for a dog may be stumbled upon by a man or woman. A quick kill or mauling results. The leopard learns how easy the kill was made and eventually turns its attention to this easily-surprised and easily-taken prey.

Although the elephant is probably the most destructive African animal to villagers and hunters alike, the leopard is often considered the most dangerous because of its small size and ferocity. The elephant has limitations when it comes to staying out of sight but the leopard's camouflage is so effective that it remains invisible against a variety of backgrounds until a man or animal walks up on it.

In recent years the bicycle has been the status symbol in remote Africa. The man who owned a bicycle had "arrived" in the eyes of his villagers. However, it offered little more protection than that afforded a walking man in big game country. Recently a native ranger cycling through Uganda's savanna country saw a leopard cub in the grass. He assumed that the mother was in the vicinity so he pedaled faster. The mother was as he feared, and leaped to his back where she clung as the man tried to shake her off without losing his balance and putting himself at her mercy. After 200 yards he managed to shake her free.

Much of the leopard's behavior under specific circumstances is quite predictable. Unlike most animals trying to avoid a hunter by running when they sense discovery, the leopard charges or leaps on the hunter the instant the hunter's eyes settle on it and the leopard knows it has been seen. J. A. Hunter twice watched hunters walk under a tree containing a hidden leopard. Each time the animal remained motionless until the hunter glanced up and saw the leopard. It sprang immediately. Each hunter avoided injury because he was expecting this action and literally shot the leopard out of the air. A flaw in the leopard's camouflage is its tendency to lie on a limb with its tail hanging off the limb. Experienced leopard hunters look for this giveaway.

Leopards seldom weigh as much as they appear to or reach the lengths one feels certain are authentic. No doubt this is because of the leopard's ferocity. A leopard seldom exceeds 135 pounds (the female some twenty pounds less) or reaches lengths of much over eight feet (including tail). Only rare leopards exceed these figures. A 1959 Loliando leopard was found to be nine feet long. (Jack O'Connor, a department editor for *Outdoor Life* magazine says this is "simply preposterous", but then O'Connor in a 1964 study of the leopard stated that he had never heard of an African man-eating leopard.) The width of a spread forepaw on the Loliando leopard was six and one-half inches. Frequent measurements are recorded of stretched specimens or skins, but the Loliando figure seems not to be beyond belief for Peter Turnbull-Kemp who prepared the definitive study, *The Leopard*. Generally the larger leopards live in Africa's equatorial jungles. Most black leopards come from these forests.

Leopards vary significantly in coloration. Black cubs can appear in the same litter with spotted ones. Leopards in their prime tend to have basic colorings from straw to reddish. Older leopards show paler colors. The leopard's spots vary from spots to rosettes to jaguar-type rosettes, the last showing a dark spot in the center of the rosette.

So effective is the leopard's marvelous camouflage that at first its effectiveness generates a feeling close to awe. The spotted coat seems to melt into almost any background. A favorite lap robe of mine is made of fabric printed with a leopard pattern. Almost any spot I place it outdoors: rocks, brush, barren soil, or grass seems to absorb it. One African farm manager hunting a raiding leopard paused before an open space. He watched a cloud of midges, or gnats, drifting along the brush line before him. Suddenly he realized that two yellow leopard eyes were staring at him from the insects. Although he had all senses attuned to the hunt he could not see the animal until it was a few feet away.

To many the leopard's eyes seem always to reflect a deep resentment or irritation. There is none of the cheetah's detached, often bored, dignity when man is close, nor the lion's disinterest. There may be no such thing in the animal world as an "evil stare," at least according to the zoologist. If there is not, the leopard's usual expression comes closer to it than that of any other member of the cat family.

Leopard cubs may be born in any month of the year. The den is usually a natural rocky cave or crevice, or a suitable spot in dense brush. The gestation period is ninety to ninety-five days, the period occasionally beginning shortly after the female approaches the male for mating. At times the female in season will drive away the male's mate and take him for her own partner.

The cubs are blind at birth and may number up to six. Although large litters seem to be common in the wild only one or two cubs are apt to survive. The mother usually eats the cubs which die.

Despite the leopard's tendency toward a solitary life the male may remain with the family and provide food to the mother and cubs if game is plentiful in the area. If game is scarce the mother usually drives the male away so he cannot compete for food.

Observations have been made of atypical family

groups which include mother, father, new cubs and the older cubs from a previous mating. The older cubs travel near but not in the family group. Leopard pairs are not rare and two may hunt together for a considerable time before splitting.

A new leopard cub is irresistible to watch. It is an awkward, pot-bellied oversize kitten, jumping at every insect and leaf movement. It goes to great lengths to launch attacks on an insect, stalking, charging, falling, snarling, and slapping recklessly, usually ending with a startled but unharmed insect.

Game wardens and others who have kept leopard cubs for a time report that they have a strong liking for warm water, both to drink and to play in. Peter Turnbull-Kemp said that his pet cub loved to join him in his bath until it ate the soap and immediately formed a dislike for these baths. Although leopards avoid water puddles rather than wet their feet and pick up grit as a result, they do not hesitate to plunge into large bodies of water and swim.

The cubs are weaned at three months. Until they are able to keep pace with their mother they are left at a selected nursery while the mother hunts. They are well disciplined and usually remain in place. It is at such times that men stumble across "orphaned cubs" and snatch them up to rush them off to a strange and most often fatal environment. Surprisingly, the mother leopard does abandon cubs with some frequency for various reasons. During his years of observing leopards in the field Peter Turnbull-Kemp said that he found numbers of leopard cubs seemingly deserted. He explained that he considered the cub truly abandoned if it was thin and showed some distress. Those cubs that were obviously well fed were left alone and he moved out of the area immediately to avoid encountering an aroused mother.

Cubs usually remain with mothers for a year and perhaps as long as eighteen months. Records exist of cubs less than six months of age killing small animals, but the chances of survival for orphaned cubs of this age are slim.

Leopard cubs show far more instinctive hunting traits than lion cubs, however, and the orphaned leopard cub has a better chance of survival than its lion counterpart. Hunting abilities develop rapidly and by the time a leopard is a year old, it frequently kills prey during a hunt directed by its mother.

The cub's extraordinary sight and hearing develop rapidly. People hear sound frequencies from about fifteen cycles per second to 20,000 per second. Leopards detect sounds in this range and on up to 45,000 cycles per second. They also have a superior ability to detect the exact spot from which the sound came.

Although the sense of smell is roughly on a par with that of other cat family members, this ability never approaches the keenness of sight and hearing. A lost puppy usually follows its mother's scent until it finds her. A lost leopard cub cannot follow its mother's scent.

Most of us learn as children that many species of wildlife do not have the capacity or inclination to return the warm affection we extend while children to them. Box turtles do not respond to cuddling. Ants have no comprehension of a pet owner's smile. Snails refuse to be petted and tamed.

I once lifted a magnetic little ball of fluff, a baby opossum, to my chest. It snuggled against me momentarily, then clamped jaws through my collar. The incident lifted my hair in fright and the jaws had to be pried apart. Later I realized that the "attack" was not belligerence but an instinctive act on the baby opossum's part to seize a secure hold for travel as it would on its mother's back.

For most of us a baby leopard is as magnetic as any potential pet could be. During its first few weeks of life it would be a delightful pet, because it is a cat and it is small, weighing little over one pound at birth. It grows quickly, however, reaching six to seven pounds in ninety days. In less than a year it weighs about fifty pounds.

Even before such weights are reached the young leopard is dangerous. By the time a captive leopard cub is two months old it is apt to make serious attacks on domestic cats and dogs. If two leopard cubs are kept together the two will fight furiously by four months of age.

At night even the best leopard pet sheds some of its domesticity and acquires instinctive predator traits of its kind. A pet leopard allowed to roam at night will probably bring grief to itself and its owner because of raids on neighboring properties. The leopard pet is a one-man pet, tolerating no liberties from others. In Peter Turnbull-Kemp's words, the pet leopard "is seldom absolutely predictable . . . He is never anything but exceedingly formidable."

A few years ago nineteen-year-old Jean Lester took one of six partially tamed leopards, kept by her father on a southern African farm, into the nearby savanna for some film sequences. Until this moment she had treated the big cats much as overgrown domestic cats. They were quiet and seemed to like her gentle wrestling. However, on location Jean saw the leopard's eyes suddenly widen. Although she had no precedent she sensed what was about to happen.

She screamed as the leopard leaped for her, the animal moving so fast that a sequence of movie film showed a smile still on her face when it reached her. It seized her waist with claws spread and sank its teeth into her side. Before she could tear herself free the leopard's teeth were in her scalp.

Her father pried the leopard's jaws apart with his bare hands. At the hospital Jean's wounds required eighty stitches to close.

Although leopards have been kept in captivity in one way or another for centuries the animal is not pet material. Few people have the capacity for adequate leopard care. Some of the liabilities which have been listed by a former leopard owner include risk of death to family members, neighbors, and neighbor's dogs, costs of feeding and veterinary services, the probable violation of game and municipal laws, and the problem of disposing of a mature leopard. Turnbull-Kemp told of one leopard owner in India who refused to turn her leopard over to a zoo when she had to leave the country. She set it free in the wild, into an environment in which it had no food-getting experience. The leopard was almost dead from starvation by the time it hid in a village hut and was burned to death by frightened villagers.

There are some of us who feel that anyone who tries to keep a leopard as a pet deserves it.

8: *The Smaller Cats*

IT COMES AS A SURPRISE TO MOST OF US TO LEARN THAT
our basic small game animals are duplicated in Africa.
The smaller cats and their prey illustrate this very
well. Africa has the equivalent of the lynx, bobcat,
hare, tree squirrel, ground squirrel, and numerous
other small animals such as porcupines which are
easily recognizable.

Africa's gray squirrel is the same one that is found
in Central Park or the Great Smoky Mountains. It was
introduced to southern Africa by Cecil Rhodes where
it thrives, as does the native bush squirrel and ground
squirrel. Bush hares, Cape hares and red rock hares
are counterparts of American rabbits and hares. These
are choice morsels for lesser members of Africa's cat
family and their habitat is more like the American
West than the tropical jungles our grade school geog-
raphy books have pictured as Africa. All of these
smaller African animals would probably thrive in the
American Southwest.

A survey of the Ngorongoro Crater—about ten by
twelve miles—made by game biologist Richard Estes

during a thirty-month period ended in mid-1965 gives an indication of the probable ratio of cat family members in any particular area of East Africa's high plains country. Of six cat species frequently observed, the dominant species was the lion with a usual sixty to seventy individuals, six leopards, about that many cheetahs, occasional caracals, numerous servals and frequently-seen African wildcats. Since many extensive observations were made at night of predator-prey relationships the ratio is probably the most accurate of such a cat ratio to date. Although numbers were probably higher than normal because of the permanent water and grass which keep thousands of prey animals there, the ratio should be representative.

The serval, *Leptailurus serval,* lives in central and southern Africa's mountains. It is Africa's counterpart to America's bobcat although it could never be mistaken for a bobcat. It is spotted with large rounded ears and a relatively long tail, at least in comparison to our bobcat. Its spots generally reflect the cheetah's spot pattern although the spots are farther apart and the coat is light rust. Its two and one-half foot length is half tail.

Africans who are familiar with all of the continent's smaller cats consider the serval to be the most beautiful of the group. Black specimens are observed often enough to prevent any particular excitement when one is observed. All of the melanistic spotted cats look solidly black at a distance but observations from a few feet away in adequate light reveal the spot pattern.

It is not quite as big as the caracal, reaching a maximum weight of thirty-four pounds. Its height is twenty inches and maximum length is fifty-four inches.

The serval's habitat includes the brushy habitat favored by the American bobcat. It hunts the thick brush and along stream banks at night. Like the bobcat it caterwauls periodically to frighten small animals and birds into movement so they can be detected and caught. Its scream, however, is not like the bobcat's, but is described variously as a weird, "How! how! how!" or a high, "Mwa! mwa! mwa!"

It is not as shy as our bobcat, however. It can be found far out on open plains at times with the nearest refuge consisting only of scattered trees hundreds of yards away. When trapped by dogs, man or wild predators it does not show the ferocity of most other members of the cat family. Perhaps for this reason it gets along well in captivity and reacts favorably to kind treatment by humans. Individual differences are pronounced and serval owners who have given their pets cause for resentment seldom change this reaction.

Although almost as big as the caracal it is not as powerful or ferocious, in this respect a departure from the American bobcat. It is at home in trees but apparently secures most prey from the ground and spends most of its time there where it hunts rodents, game

Serval

birds and small birds. It occasionally takes poultry and antelope fawns. Hyraxes are favorite food and in farm areas the serval probably serves man well by containing hyrax numbers.

Litters of one to three kittens are born blind after a gestation period of sixty-eight to seventy-four days. The den is found most often in abandoned antbear burrows, old anthills or other suitable underground passages.

The caracal, *Felis caracal,* is the African lynx, its kinship to the Canadian lynx readily apparent from its tufted ears and general shape. The lynxes are among the most widespread of cat family members, being found in all parts of the world except Australia, South America and Malaya.

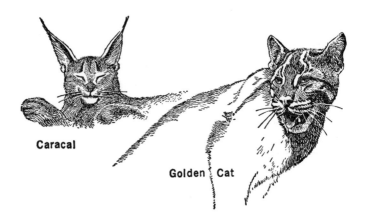

Caracal

Golden Cat

The caracal's brilliant red rust coloring is distinctive among African cats and is easily mistaken in tall grass for the steenbok. It is widely distributed in South Africa and suitable bush lands and veld north through Kenya. Although common in many areas it is totally unknown to most Africans because of its secretive habits. It hunts occasionally during daylight but most hunting is done at night. It avoids settled areas except for occasional depredations on lambs and goat kids.

It is a medium-sized cat weighing up to forty pounds and reaching shoulder heights up to eighteen inches. Length is from sixteen to thirty inches.

Its beauty is deceiving for it is remarkably savage, a characteristic not shared by the Canadian lynx. When wounded or trapped it can be dangerous to man, a characteristic sometimes shared by the American bobcat. It has a longer tail than either Canadian lynx or bobcat. It is about nine inches and reaches to its heels.

Its prey is almost any bird or animal which it can capture. It has taken the tawny eagle and martial eagle from roost limbs, both formidable birds. The latter preys upon small antelopes. It reportedly attacks setting ostriches, the largest living bird which reaches heights of eight feet and whose powerful legs can easily knock down a man. Small antelope, gazelles, hares and rodents are taken with some regularity.

The black-footed cat, *Microfelis nigripes*, is probably the rarest African cat and although it is difficult to decide which species is the handsomest of the cat family, this beautiful animal must be first or second to most observers. It does not look like a wildcat, but resembles closely a long-haired domestic cat with unusual markings.

Its face is broad and gives no clue to its latent fury. Elongated black spots are found over the whole body. Those at the back of the neck are almost stripes and those on the shoulders become transverse stripes. These black spots fade to brown as the cat grows older. Most of the hair is at least an inch long and on some parts of the body reaches lengths of two inches. The general color is tawny, a rich, warm, soft color which invites a hand to reach out to smooth the luxurious hair. To do so, however, would bring a reaction similar to slapping an American bobcat's face barehanded.

Although it is about the size of a large tomcat it regularly kills sheep weighing four times its own weight. Sheepherders have observed such attacks often enough to authenticate the standard tactic. It leaps to the throat and fastens its teeth into neck tissues solidly enough to close the windpipe. The sheep dies of strangulation. Only then does this fierce little cat relax and withdraw its oversized canine teeth. Blood oozing from the tooth punctures after death gives rise to the supposition among most observers that the jugular vein is severed and causes death; however, it is doubtful that this occurs except by chance since the holes in neck tissues made by the teeth are effectively plugged until after death and the cat relinquishes its hold.

Although some reports restrict it to Botswana, South West Africa, it has a slightly larger territory which includes the arid western parts of South Africa as far south as the Eastern Cape Province, as far east as the edges of Orange Free State and the Transvaal. All of these are political subdivisions of South Africa. It may possibly be found in the southwestern edge of Rhodesia which borders South Africa to the north.

Like many other small animals it uses abandoned anthills and the holes of springhares and other burrowing animals for its daytime resting place and den. The kittens are further developed at birth than domestic cats and grow faster so that they are able to secure their own food relatively quickly. The male of this species interbreeds freely with female domestic cats, as does that of the African wildcat; however, domestic tomcats never seem to have the nerve to risk the displeasure of the females of these wild species.

Africa's golden cat, *Profelis aurata cottoni,* is almost a miniature of the American cougar or mountain lion. It is about twice the size of a housecat and apparently has at least two color phases, a golden-brown and a bluish-gray, neither of which seems to be a product of sex, age, or environment. These color phases are pronounced in such diverse American wildlife as the cougar and screech owl. It may or may not have darker spots on undersurfaces and flanks.

Because of its secretive habits and thick forest or jungle habitat, little is known about this cat. It is found in Africa's equatorial jungles from the Atlantic eastward to Kenya's high rain forest, the Aberdares north of Nairobi.

Southern Asia has a golden cat which, except to the taxonomist who must find the ultimate detail to allow differentiation between animals in order to assign specie names, is identical for all practical purposes.

Naturalist E. P. Gee, author of *The Wildlife of India*, purchased a kitten of India's golden cat, *Felis temminckii*, from a small animal dealer. Fortunately for Gee the kitten had been taken probably before its eyes opened. As a result it quickly adopted Gee as its mother and loved to suckle his ear lobes or knead his lap with its claws.

Gee allowed it complete freedom and the golden cat roved into the nearby jungle daily. It always returned promptly at Gee's call.

It grew swiftly. By the time it reached a length of three feet nine inches Gee became concerned for its safety since local hunters roved the jungle and would not hesitate to put an arrow into the cat if they saw it. Then, too, Gee knew that adult golden cats which reach lengths slightly over four feet, prey on goats, sheep and even buffalo calves.

There was no place in India to release his pet safely because of the high human populations. He decided to give it to the London Zoo where it adapted itself readily to life there. Later when one of Gee's nieces visited the zoo she wrote that the cat "almost realized" that she knew his former master. The big cat played with her hair braids through the cage bars.

India's golden cats prefer the high mountain country, but Africa's golden cat seems to have the versatility of its closest look-alike, the American cougar. Both the latter are equally at home in hot, humid tropical forests and high mountain country.

In parts of West Africa the golden cat ranks as significantly in local religious rituals and beliefs as does the leopard. Ivan T. Sanderson, collecting and studying wildlife in Nigeria, tried to obtain a golden cat for his project. Every hunter asked replied that he had never heard of the animal. When Sanderson saw golden cat fur pieces in a chief's ceremonial costume and asked about them, he was told that they came from a far country. Sanderson had no success offering substantial payments for a golden cat.

Finally Sanderson was initiated into the leopard society and began to understand the veneration accorded the animal. From this point he was able to influence Africans who helped him obtain two skins, one of which was killed only three miles from his camp. The hunters who killed this golden cat disappeared into the jungle immediately after their success and did not return for four days. Sanderson never did obtain a skull which plays an important part in the local religious life.

Africa's wildcat, *Felis lybica*, is the ancestor of domestic cats and has a wide range from South Africa to Israel to the island of Sardinia. The Egyptians are credited with domesticating and deifying the cat and many mummified specimens of this animal have been found in their tombs.

It looks like a large "brindle" or "tiger" cat, gray with indistinct darker stripes set vertically along its sides and horizontally on the legs. An observer has to look closely to distinguish the two physical characteristics: shorter tail and sand-colored ear backs. It reaches lengths of thirty-six inches and weights of eight and one-half pounds.

It is known by a variety of regional names in Africa: gray wildcat, Kaffir cat, *vaalboskat*, taita gray wildcat, and *paka pori*, and although seldom seen it is not perturbed by nearby villages or cities. It interbreeds frequently with domestic cats. The unsuspecting cat owner's first knowledge of this occurs when his cat's litter turns out to be a ball of spitting, clawing, fighting kittens with none of the calm temperament of their mother. Such kittens seldom become trustful of humans. In its stronger blood lines this cat and close hybridizations appear to be untameable.

Gestation period for the wildcat is about fifty-six days and litters usually number two to three although rare litters have contained as many as five. The wildcat mother makes her den in a rock crevice or animal burrow.

It has an appetite for poultry although its normal prey consists of rodents, birds, snakes, insects and occasional ripened fruits. It has been known to take young antelope.

Its calls are not dissimilar to those of the domestic cat although its "meow" is harsher. Its mating yowls are virtually indistinguishable from those of domestic cats.

America has no counterpart but Europe has an almost indistinguishable look-alike, *Felis silvestris grampia*. This European wildcat can still be found in Europe's more inaccessible terrain such as Scotland's mountains where it has increased over recent decades. In Scotland it seldom stirs during daylight, preferring to remain out of sight in rocky terrain. Here it reaches lengths of two feet nine inches but one Scottish record measures a foot longer.

An early English naturalist, Pennant, wrote in 1776, "This animal may be called the British tiger; it is the fiercest and most destructive beast we have; making dreadful havoc among our poultry, lambs and kids."

There are several cat-like African animals which are generally referred to as cats but are not. These belong to the Viverrid group of the carnivores, the order which includes the cat and dog families as well as others. The Viverrids have some of the physical appearance of the cats as well as such Mustelids as martens. Their noses are pointed and tails are long. Claws may or may not be retractile and they may walk on the toes or balls of their feet. Genets and civet cats are frequently considered members of Africa's cat family although they are not. For this reason they are described as follows:

The genets, *Genetta felina, G. tigrina, G. rubiginosa,* look much like the New World's ringtail "cat" which is the raccoon's closest relative. Their tails are long, bushy, and pointed with seven to ten rings. There are three of them in eastern and southern Africa, the small-spotted genet, the large-spotted genet, and the rusty-spotted genet. All their body patterns are similar, irregular lines running from the face along the top of the shoulders and breaking up into lines of spots along the body. In the Congo Basin genet skins are popular with witch doctors or magicians who use them as part of their costumes. In the Zambezi River Valley I saw genet skins included in a witch doctor's bag of herbs and magic components.

Genets are efficient rat killers, a fact well known to ancient Egyptians who used them as mousers more frequently than cats. Genets are popular pets throughout Africa and when captured young they become affectionate pets and show remarkable intelligence. Their growls and spitting sound exactly like those of a housecat.

Like America's ringtail, which the genet resembles, adult genets have an empathy toward people. Joy Adamson in *Living Free* told of a female genet coming into camp to eat scraps left by her pet lions. When

Joy's husband flashed a light on the genet she ignored it and continued eating. One night he was awakened by plates falling from the table. The genet had come to eat the rest of his supper, bits of cheese and roast guinea. Again she ignored the Adamsons and made herself at home as long as food was available. She came back night after night and remained friendly as long as the lions were not around.

At one camp the Adamsons found a genet attracted to the large whisky moths which cluster on bottles and glasses to drink from them. As soon as the night light was put out the genet came quickly to catch these swarming moths.

At times the genets are merciless little killers. Like weasels and wolves they are excited by their first kill and continue to kill every prey within reach, eating only the head and fleshy parts of the breasts in the case of chickens. Once inside a pen of chickens a genet is apt to kill all of them before leaving. Their claws are semi-retractile, enabling them to climb easily and spend considerable time in trees where they take daytime naps and rob roosts at night.

Three genet kittens are found in the average litter though on rare occasions there is a fourth. In South Africa the spring months of September and October are the most common months of birth.

Africa's civet, *Viverra civetta*, looks much like the genet but is much larger, standing fifteen inches high and three and one-half feet long. It has a peculiar arched posture when it walks so that its high curved back makes it look bigger than it is. Its face seems to have been made in the same mold used for the raccoon and its black face mask is virtually the same. Its tail is ringed. Stripes run along the neck and hindquarters while rows of spots run along the ribs and shoulders. Its background coloration is a yellow-tinged gray except for solid black on parts of the undersurfaces, principally the throat.

Like the genet it is principally a nocturnal animal and is seldom seen in the wild for that reason. Its diet is as versatile as the genet's. It eats carrion, small animals, birds, toads, snakes, snails, insects, eggs, fruit and anything else at hand which is edible. It is not as good a climber as the genet but will destroy poultry in pens which allow its entrance. Its claws are not retractile and show plainly in its tracks in contrast to genet tracks which, like all cat tracks except the cheetah's, do not normally show claw marks.

The civet selects a certain spot for its droppings and returns regularly to this spot to deposit droppings.

During daylight hours it naps in thick grass or brush or in the burrows of antbears or porcupines. These burrows serve it as a den and a litter consists of two or three young. When calling its young or to another civet it sounds a series of low coughs, but when harassed by dogs it growls deeply.

Peter Turnbull-Kemp calls the civet "exceedingly inoffensive." He has caught several by hand when they were in small areas from which they could not easily escape. Although they growl and make feints at biting, a person grabbing the scruff of the neck has little trouble capturing them safely.

The larger cats and other predators take them occasionally. Leopards habitually pluck the hair from the civet's body before eating it. Because of its lack of belligerence its scent glands seem vital for its survival.

The civet is another animal exploited by man with cruelty (from the human viewpoint at least) to satisfy the whims of vanity and fashion. There is no way to estimate the number of women the world over who loudly proclaim their distaste of cruelty to animals yet are the basic cause of such treatment. They are well insulated from guilt feelings, however, because of ignorance.

In this case, the civet was the source of a commercial product from Zanzibar and coastal East Africa called "civet," a base of many perfumes. To obtain this civet, suppliers kept thousands of these animals in cages so small that they did not permit the animals to turn around. This allowed the most efficient extraction of a secretion from the anal glands which looks like rancid butter but has a strong odor. This is sealed in cow horns and shipped to perfume manufacturers over the world as commercial "civet." It is the best fixative for perfume essences known to man and is used in the most expensive brands.

Perhaps this life was intolerable to the civet. Perhaps it was not. In any event much of the meat we eat, pork, beef and chicken, comes from animals and poultry restricted to feed lots small enough to discourage exercise and encourage constant eating. This, too, allows more efficient production of animal products.

9: *Leopard Men and Lion Men*

DOES CANNIBALISM EXIST TODAY IN AFRICA? YES, IT DOES.
C. A. W. Guggisberg, whose twenty-five years of
study and observations have made him the world
authority on the lion, says that cannibalism "is by no
means extinct." Modern Africa with its skyscrapers,
miniskirts, Mercedes taxis, television and other products of today's world seems to refute the existence
of this ancient custom. Statesmen and columnists
who see Africa from Nairobi's Thorn Tree sidewalk
tables smile knowingly at the suggestion that men and
women are still eaten. Everybody knows that cannibalism was a part of darkest Africa. Unfortunately,
it still exists in today's Africa, as does witchcraft and
secret societies such as the lion men and the leopard
societies. The leopard society in Sierra Leone is still
concerned with ritual cannibalism and as a consequence has terrified neighboring tribes from which
victims are taken.

Much to his surprise Jean-Pierre Hallet found he
had eaten pot roast made from a young Congolese
woman thrown out by her husband because she could
not produce children. This happened in 1950 during

Hallet's work as a colonial administrator in the Congo. He had been instructed to investigate evidence of cannibalism which formed a prominent part in rituals of the *Bwamé* secret society, but had had no success when he stumbled into a jungle camp where several young boys lived in isolation prior to ritual circumcision.

The pot of meat whetted the hungry Hallet's appetite and he asked what was being cooked. The answer was porcupine, two of them. He was given several chunks on a banana leaf plate. He ate them with relish, remarking on their tenderness and taste.

Later that night Hallet asked details of the ritual the boys were to undergo and learned from one boy by accident what the pot roast consisted of. When the wife was thrown out of the neighboring village the boy's uncle found her, cut her throat and brought her into the camp where her flesh was cut off and her bones were burned into ashes for ritual use. When Hallet asked what had happened to her flesh the boy casually replied that they had just eaten her. Then, realizing he had given the secret away to a government official, the boy became terrified. Instead of jailing them Hallet tried to convince them of the seriousness of this crime and made them all swear an oath never to repeat the act. Hallet believed they might have kept their promise for a time.

The Congo's *Bwamé* secret society undoubtedly received new life with the exit of Belgian administrators in 1960 and tribal power regained dominance in the newly-independent Congo's back country. Other secret societies flourish, certainly more vigorously than in America and Europe where business and social leaders belong to tamer secret societies. Among the most widespread of Africa's secret societies or forces are the lion men and leopard men.

The lion men seem to be less well known to us because mention is seldom made in our literature on Africa. However, they are a more formidable group than the leopard societies because of their unrestrained terror in certain parts of Africa.

A lion man is not easy to define since the term may mean a "werelion," comparable to the werewolf of European legend, in one area, a murder society, an extortion group, or a witch doctor's power grab in another.

Probably the best-liked tribe in East Africa is the Wakamba tribe. It lives in south central Kenya in relatively poor land where a successful life requires more wisdom than luck. As a result the Wakamba can match wits with anyone. It was my good fortune recently to go on a number of game-viewing explorations in East Africa with a Wakamba, John Wambua, as our guide. He could speak six languages and could handle English far better than any of us. He was a graduate of African wildlife management courses which had provided him with quick answers to our detailed questions, and his ever-present sense of humor kept us chuckling even when we were pushing him along a Kenyan road to get a balky motor started. His brother graduated recently as an M. D. from the University of Michigan. In short here was a man in step with today's world.

Yet some of John Wambua's relatives living in traditional tribal country still had to put up with witch doctors whose weapons for subduing villagers included a black powder made from certain plants. This valuable powder, so the witch doctors convinced believers, protected a person from attack by lions. Those witch doctors able to use black magic let it be known that they could turn themselves into lions at any time by smearing a special powder on their faces and eating some powdered lion parts. Each time a lion kills a person in the area, many villagers are convinced the killer was a man who had turned himself into a lion. The desired result of more respect and contributions to the witch doctor follows.

Similar extortions are made by a few native religious heads, witch doctors, throughout Africa where the lion and leopard are commonly found.

In 1946, a rash of lion men murders occurred in central Tanganyika, now Tanzania. Reports were in all the East African papers. Authorities were reminded that the area had been afflicted with lion men for years. In 1920, some 200 people were killed near Singida town. An official from the British government assumed the deaths were the work of lions and began shooting the animals. Then he was told that ordinary lions had nothing to do with the murders. Lion men had done the work. Investigations showed that extortion by witch doctors was rampant and when a person refused to contribute he was visited by a lion man.

After one such murder, villagers followed the killer's trail immediately and caught a young man dressed in a lion's skin. His hands and feet fitted into the feet of the skin. He confessed that he was a hired killer in the employ of a witch doctor who assigned him to kill people that relatives or enemies wanted killed.

One man told the investigators that he had been kidnaped while very young and reared with other boys who had been collected for training in killing with knives under the guise of lion men. This man, however, had made a miserable failure of his first assignment to kill and was kicked out of the lion men group.

Drugs, especially hashish, were commonly used. One man explained how he had drugged a girl and convinced her that she had changed into a lion. He rented her to anyone who wanted a killing performed at thirty shillings ($4.20 in today's U. S. currency).

Tanganyika police captured one unfortunate lion man who as a child had had half of each foot cut off. He had been trained to walk on all fours like a lion. Whenever his master was ready for him to kill in the guise of a lion man, he was given drugs and sewed into a lion's skin. The maimed man escaped soon after capture, much to police embarrassment and renewed such terror in local people that they were extremely reluctant to talk about it for fear of retribution.

In 1957, a Nairobi newspaper reported the results of a trial of two women and a man connected with a lion man murder in the same area of Tanganyika. The three had hired a lion man to kill a five-year-old girl who was snatched from her mother's arms and carried into the brush. Only a few body parts were found the next day.

At subsequent lion men trials, a number of the defendants were women. Four women were involved in hiring a lion man to murder a woman relative of one defendant. The two had quarreled over money. Three other women hired a lion man to kill a boy because he was disobedient and because his father would not support one of the women.

In the Congo, at least, the lion men are supplanted by the *Anyoto*, or society of leopard men. Belgian administrators of the Congo before it became independent, believed the leopard society originated in the Congo's Ituri Forest. It soon became a terrorist organization without equal in any other country. Many deaths and mutilations were merely the result of initiation requirements and victims, usually women or children because they offered little resistance, were selected without regard. However, a few leopard societies required that the killer select a relative.

There was little doubt among most natives and investigators, that the leopard men were men and not animals. Their costumes were not especially authentic, but they were frightening, even paralyzing, to the person confronted and about to be killed. Shirts with hoods were made of bark cloth and daubed with black rings and spots in imitation of the leopard's pelage. A real leopard's tail was usually used and tied to a belt which also held an earthen pot used to blow across in imitation of a leopard's snarl, a knife, a metal bracelet with four short knives that jutted between the fingers when the hand formed a fist, and a stick carved on the end in the shape of leopard pads to leave imprints in the soil.

All these items were calculated to convince anyone who found the body that leopards had done the work. The leopard men spoiled the effect, however, by their superstitions. They cut the breasts from females as proof of having performed the killing and later ate them. Usually the eyes were torn out and boiled in a ritual brew in which the metal claw was immersed. The leopard man drank this concoction in the belief that it enabled him to see better in the night.

During the following days, the killer was an ordinary villager doing nothing to attract attention to him. The killer had no qualms about his grisly work, feeling that if people thought a leopard did the work the animal was guilty and he was not.

About 1900 the leopard men were at the height of their power in the Congo, killing estimated thousands annually. The year after the Belgians took control of the Congo in 1909, over fifty leopard men killers were caught and hanged in one town. Jean-Pierre Hallet, who worked may years for the colonial government estimated that a hundred leopard men victims were taken annually for the next twenty years. In 1934 leopard men took forty-two victims in ninety days in the Congo's Beni region.

Ivan T. Sanderson, a Scotsman whose experiences as a naturalist and animal collector have made him known to readers of many countries, joined a Nigerian leopard society in the 1930's. Among the information he acquired was the importance of leopard whiskers in the society's usage. Any leopard killed in the area and turned over to local skinners was minus its whiskers within a few moments after the men went to work. When trouble broke out in Sanderson's camp following the first leopard skinning he soon learned the reason. One man, whose father was a secret society official, had pulled out all the leopard's whiskers. The other men believed he was about to poison them.

Since he had heard stories of poisoning by leopard or lion whiskers before, Sanderson determined to investigate the truth of these. He secured other leopard whiskers and tasted them without swallowing. He could detect no poisonous quality. Then he mixed chopped whiskers in a mash of corn and bananas and offered this to a chimpanzee. The chimp looked at this with some suspicion but took a bite. Then he stuck a forefinger into the food and felt the whisker sections. He spat out the food in his mouth, dumped the remainder on the ground and stomped it.

Later a monkey ate some of the preparation and died a few weeks later. Sanderson then performed a detailed examination of its digestive tract. He found nothing unusual at first. Then he noticed many tiny cysts deep in the stomach wall. Upon opening them he found that each one contained a single section of leopard whisker unchanged by digestive juices.

Sanderson believes that Africans who are considered to have been poisoned by leopard whiskers and subsequently died of "tiger-for-belly," actually died of ruptured stomach walls and peritonitis.

What would happen if you jetted into one of Africa's ultra-modern airports today and asked a taxi driver or policeman to direct you to the nearest leopard society or cannibal tribe? He would stare aghast or double with laughter. Most Africans have not the slightest knowledge of either subject, nor of their existence.

What would happen if you asked a New York taxi driver to take you to the nearest headquarters of Murder, Incorporated?

10: *Photographing Africa's Lions and Cats*

THE LION IS PROBABLY THE EASIEST LARGE WILD ANIMAL in the world to photograph in its natural setting. Almost any photographic safari provides more than enough opportunity to photograph it from the safety of vehicles only a few feet away. Few activities can equal the excitement for outdoor lovers of African big game photography.

A photographic safari has suddenly become available to the average American. Total costs are measured in fractions of former rates and air fares can be paid in monthly installments after the trip. An African trip is now as available for a school teacher as it once was for the millionaire big game hunter. At this writing the economy excursion round-trip jet fare from New York to East Africa's big game country: Nairobi, Lusaka, Lindi, Beira, Bulawayo, Dar Es Salaam, is roughly the amount of an average schoolteacher's monthly pay check.

We learned a significant amount about big game photography before we reached Africa. The first hazard to adequate photography was the jet airliner that took us there. The quiet vibration loosened several tiny screws on cameras and telephoto lenses. We were surprised at this although we expected loose screws after every day of Land Rover bouncing. The remedy was a simple five-minute screw-tightening session each evening. Our tool was a small sewing machine screw driver. When we found it necessary, we filed the blade slightly to fit the smallest visible screw. A small triangular file is worth its weight in any luggage headed for the field. One simple "lock" for camera screws is a drop of clear fingernail polish on each screw head.

The next biggest camera crippler is dust. You don't need a dust storm, but only a few days of invisible dust jarred from a vehicle or light plane to infiltrate camera mechanisms and jam them. There are two remedies: A daily dusting of the camera body with a dime store paint brush and habitual use of a plastic freezer bag over the camera.

A frustrating effort is to try brushing all the dust from a lens with a lens brush. Static electricity holds a certain amount on the lens surface after careful brushing by the finest sable lens brush on the market. Buy an ear syringe at the drugstore and blow all the dust away. Use both hands for this, aiming the tip with one and squeezing with the other.

A plastic bag used as a dust protector is probably the cheapest camera insurance available. You need no lens caps when using the bag to cover lens and camera.

When an animal pops up the bag can be snapped off. Such fast camera work dictates pre-focusing at the expected range and an exposure reading measured on the trees, brush or plains around you.

Perhaps my most rewarding shot due to this precaution, occurred early one morning in the jungle of acacia trees and wild gardenia separating Tanzania's Lake Manyara and the east face of the Great Rift Wall. We were in a Volkswagen bus easing along an auto track liberally sprinkled with fresh elephant droppings.

As the vegetation opened up I took a new light reading and focused for fifty feet, using a speed setting somewhere in the middle of the dial which kept most objects in focus from about twenty feet to infinity. A fast shutter speed would have drastically cut this depth of field.

Suddenly we were among a small herd of young bull elephants. The closest one was busy with an exercise never seen in the zoo and infrequently in the wild. He was astride an anthill and scraping back and forth with enough vigor to flatten the anthill's upper surface.

Then I remembered having read of an elephant's most satisfying moment. He was scraping ticks off his belly and the fact that we had intruded upon his private moment did not deter him from a few more delightful seconds.

I shot quickly without taking time to check focus

or light reading. Before the second shot I did check these but by then he was gone. Later I found the photo to be in better focus than I could hope for through no effort of mine other than having been cautioned months before by a professional photographer to constantly keep focus and exposure set for your surroundings.

Another key to a successful fast camera is a shoulder stock (pistol grips), not a gun stock. The latter's weight and bulk limit action. A simple twelve-inch stock with two pistol grips is ideal and can be easily disassembled for packing. After repeated tests my personal preferences called for the cable release trigger to be mounted in the forward grip. I squeezed the trigger with a left finger and operated the focus ring with my right fingers, the latter also serving to steady the camera. This stock retails for $8 to $12.

African animals have no sympathy for tripod users who produce photographs of ideal sharpness under ideal conditions. There is little time for setting up a tripod. When shooting photos from a vehicle or boat, the motor vibration is transmitted through the tripod to the camera. The body absorbs this vibration when the camera is held at the shoulder.

A handy method of steadying your camera without a tripod is a bean bag. Almost any small cloth bag which can hold about one quart or more of dried beans, peas or grain will make a solid base for your camera. Even sand or gravel can be used if necessary.

Place the bag atop the car or on a window sill and set your camera hand firmly into it. The bag is generally more versatile than a tripod under these conditions. The engine must be turned off before shooting, however.

What type of lens is best for shooting from a moving vehicle, aircraft, or motorboat? A telephoto lens is the worst choice since it magnifies movement and vibration, as well as the image. A normal lens, usually 50 to 55 mm, is still not adequate to stop blurring caused by vibration in most situations. The best lens to use from a vibrating base, consequently, is the wide-angle lens, usually the 35 mm lens or less. This decreases the image size because it crowds more area into the picture but this is usually a far better compromise than a blurred image of any size. The smaller images on wide-angle exposed film can be enlarged as needed.

If you have no wide-angle lens but only your regular lens, vibration blurring can be decreased by hand holding while standing on your feet and supporting the camera's weight entirely with your hands. Do not attempt to steady the camera by leaning against a window, railing, or bulkhead since any part of the vibrating vehicle will transmit vibrations to the camera. If the situation permits, insist that the automobile or boat motor be shut down until photos are taken. Use the fastest practical shutter speed, i.e., shoot at 1/500 of a second if light and shallow depth of field permit.

Where do you aim your viewfinder when shooting animals? Always focus on the eye, if it is visible. A sharp eye and fuzzy hindparts usually produce a good photograph. The opposite situation makes a poor one.

The African or any sun provides an unsuspected hindrance to camera users, especially those with eye-glasses. Side light creeps in past the eye and obscures the viewfinder image that prevents accurate focusing. If you do not wear glasses a large rubber viewfinder, surrounding the eye cuts out side light. Glasses wearers need more. I used a friend's hand: "Quick, give me a shade!", many times but this is inadequate. The African bush hat, a floppy brimmed canvas head piece, is good since the soft brim can be pulled close to the camera. An ideal shade would be a black cloth covering camera, head and shoulders like that used by early photographers. It must be heavy, however, because of the wind. I tried a blue bandanna taped to the camera but the wind kept blowing it off my head. A poor item of apparel for the serious photographer is the hard brimmed "Aussie" hat or pith helmet. We were satisfied, however, that a cloth baseball cap is fairly adequate for most African photography.

A handy camera case for the field is a fisherman's canvas vest. We managed to easily fit lenses, shades, extra film and even snacks into the four large pockets on these vests. Such items are always readily accessible.

For travel we left our conventional camera cases at home and packed all important camera equipment in a lightweight plastic briefcase-type bag purchased at the drugstore. Sides were reinforced with corrugated cardboard. The advantage to such a thin case is that it is not only practical to carry anywhere, even to meals, but opening it allows immediate access to all items. A conventional camera case is relatively heavy, bulky and by its shape requires many items to be stacked upon each other.

Perhaps the one precaution in which all professionals are in agreement for any photographic trip is alternate equipment. Additional insurance against breakage is achieved by carrying identical cameras so that all supplementary lenses will fit either.

For us this meant two Yashica TL Super 35 mm cameras from one of the national camera discount houses advertised in the photography magazines. Such items were new with all warranties and cost less than two-thirds the prices found in camera shops.

Lenses included a 300 mm telephoto which gave over five power magnification. Our alternate telephoto lens system consisted of a 135 mm lens of less than three power magnification but ideal for many middle distance shots. When a 3X extender was coupled with the 135 the combination made a 405 mm lens, or almost eight power. When the 3X extender was coupled with the regular 50 mm lens on the camera the result was a 150 mm lens, or with the 300 mm lens the result was 900 mm. The latter combination allowed magnification of over eighteen power but a serious loss in sharpness. Extenders also come in 2X and 2.5X sizes, the X designating power of magnification. Their chief limitation is that they severely reduce available light.

Can a relatively cheap camera take adequate photos? Yes, it can but only under ideal conditions. You can take a sharper photo in bright light with some $20 cameras on a tripod and using a cable release than with a Hasselblad or Leica costing over $500 hand-held by a careless photographer.

There is a good reason why professionals spend extra money for expensive cameras, however. As a rule these are built sturdily with smaller tolerances in workmanship. The $20 camera may or may not function for years. The $500 camera is built to last through decades of heavy usage. Lens quality generally varies to a lesser degree than camera construction.

There is one indispensable filter for color film in Africa, the American Southwest, or anywhere in the world as far as many professionals are concerned. This is the haze, or skylight, filter. It imparts a slight reddish tone to the photograph, in effect restoring rich color lost to a strong desert sun or eclipsed by an overcast. It cuts distant haze ordinarily invisible to the naked eye but apt to be recorded by a naked lens. Many professionals put the haze filter on and leave it for the life of the camera.

Even more important for African and other sunny shooting is a lens shade. When a shade is not used strong light from the side or front enters the lens barrel, bounces around and washes out the film's potential color and sharpness. A lens shade allows shooting into the sun, not literally but with the sun behind the target, thus making dramatic shots from often average subjects. The sun must not shine directly into the lens.

Does the hot African sun do anything to film? Not if reasonable care is taken. Exposed film deteriorates in a few weeks in a hot climate, or in a few hours in an automobile glove compartment. Never store film in baggage exposed to the sun or other heat, and *never, never* drop mailing containers of film in mail boxes which will be in the sun before pick up. I had no heat damage among fifty rolls shot on the safari. Earlier I had serious heat damage to rolls shot in Alaska.

While we're on this, do not have film developed in Africa. Bring it home. A game warden and Kenyan citizen, told me he once took some spectacular movie footage and sent it to a South African commercial developer. In return he received rolls of blank film with a note, "Sorry, your camera is broken." He was a skilled photographer and knew better. The firm had confiscated the big game footage for subsequent sale, a much cheaper method than employing staff photographers.

A general rule to keep in the back of your mind while on safari is to tend toward faster shutter speeds on SLR cameras whenever possible instead of slower ones. A faster speed allows a larger aperture for focusing than a slow speed and consequent faster focusing. In most cases the critical factor is not how fast you can draw a bead on the target but how fast you can focus on the target if it pops up in an unexpected location.

If you have trouble getting a quick sight on an animal with a telephoto mount take a suggestion from the Army's "quick kill" technique for fast shooting taught to infantrymen. Essentially shooting by "instinct" or along the line of sight, the quick kill technique does not allow time for conventional sighting but only along the barrel with both eyes open.

The modification of this technique for the camera shoulder stock requires the index finger of the forward hand to be pointed at the target. The second finger is used to trigger the cable release. Instinct allows relatively accurate finger pointing at an object and the telephoto-camera axis tends to line up automatically.

As a practical matter few animals move fast enough to make the technique rewarding. Flying birds, however, do encourage this extra effort to get on target.

The 35 mm cameras remain the most versatile cameras for most of us. The SLR, single lens reflex, has greatest versatility since almost limitless combinations of lenses can be purchased for it. Most SLR's have through-the-lens metering. Exposure problems are reduced when the meter takes the light reading through the lens. On telephoto lens you can get accurate readings of an animal standing in shade many yards away.

Who makes the best cameras? My personal belief is that no American or German camera maker can produce a camera equal to the Japanese product in the same price range. I have used all three countries' products over many years. If this statement is hard to believe, ask any professional photographer who uses 35 mm equipment extensively.

What film works best in Africa? Almost any. Photographic conditions in East and South Africa are identical with those in the American West and Southwest. I have been enthusiastic about ektachrome X for years because of its richness and ease of home development. In an area of strong sun and high altitudes such as parts of Africa it is easy to overexpose. Ektachrome X tends to hold rich color and its speed of ASA 64 is fast enough for most photography. I use high speed ektachrome with telephoto lenses since these reduce the light available. This film has a normal speed of ASA 160. I shoot it at ASA 640 and "push" or adjust the developing process, which is a kitchen sink operation requiring no darkroom. (I am not a professional photographer.) Corrections can be made for over or underexposures in subsequent rolls. Photographers shooting film at higher speeds who do not develop their own, can send film to a custom processor advertised in the photo magazines with a note giving the speed at which the film was shot. The popular Kodachrome II film has a speed of 25 and Kodachrome X, a speed of 64.

A disturbing but all-too-common sight in Africa is that of a visitor shooting with a borrowed or brand new camera. Such photographers deserve the poor results they get. Few of us take a trip to Africa often enough so doesn't it make sense to take camera equipment to the zoo or barnyard and test everything on similar animals before the trip? If the camera tends to overexpose you can allow for this. Then shoot another test roll and check the results until you are absolutely pleased with the results. Ten dollars spent here can make a vital difference in several hundred dollars' worth of African exposures.

Photographers on safari have an important advantage over the guns-only hunter. All of us have certain peeves. Close to the top of my list is the hunter who takes a peculiar pride in climbing aboard a champagne jet for a few hours' ride to Africa, rushes out to shoot a trophy already spotted by a professional hunter, then jets home hours later. There is really nothing wrong with this except that it jars my feeling about the use of the outdoors. A trophy is not the real safari objective for most of us. Enjoying outdoor Africa is.

Kenya put a crimp in the jet-set hunter's haste recently. If you want to shoot the relatively rare rhino you must book a five-week safari in order to get a license. Buffalo and most antelope require only a two-week safari. A three-week safari allows you two of elephant, leopard or lion and a buffalo. A month's safari allows licenses for taking all four species.

But the cameraman can hunt all these the first day he enters game habitat. No licenses are required. He can operate in hunting territory or game reserves. He watches wildlife during its normal behavior at relatively close range and soon learns that reserve wildlife is not gun shy or vehicle shy.

A sizable number of "great white" hunters are in fact only familiar with spoor and distant views of bobbing buttocks. Now after years of hunting bobbing buttocks I have added photography and found that my pleasure and excitement have risen significantly.

Modern Africa has a surprising similarity to much of America. European tourists come to the American West hoping to be charged by Indians on horseback. Americans and Europens go to modern Africa hoping to see natives spearing lions. There is little of this part of ancient Africa left. Even the Masai in Tanzania are jailed for posing as naked warriors. Most Africans have seen in their lifetimes far less big game than many safari visitors see in a day. Movies, rather than a life in the bush, educate today's average African about his fascinating continent.

I asked our driver, John Wambua, what the Swahili name was for the curtains of vines and lianas hanging from Lake Manyara strangler figs. He grinned.

"We call them Tarzan ropes."

Epilogue: Wildlife and Politics

BY THE TIME ONE READS THIS OR SIMILAR BOOKS HE knows a good deal more about African lions, leopards and smaller cats than the vast majority of Africans will ever learn about these subjects. Far more Americans and Europeans have seen these animals in the flesh in zoos than have Africans in the wild, or in zoos.

Few Africans have the opportunity to know or see their wildlife. Few Africans travel farther than the nearest town and interests end at the markets where they sell their farm products.

Consequently, the expert tracker or safari guide is more apt to be a non-African than a local man. A few local citizens have retained the motivations and skills which make them incomparable teachers of African natural history, but the overwhelming majority lost those skills years, or generations, ago. Today the outsider leaves Africa with the conclusion that most Africans north and west of Rhodesia aspire only to have a job with the status symbol of a white shirt, an *assimilado* with adequate arrogance to subdue the less sophisticated people around him. They seem to believe that any job with a white shirt means ample rewards with minimum work. No man likes to be reminded that he is not adequately motivated to achieve the affluence he desires, yet there is no way of concealing this glaring weakness through much of today's Africa.

South Africans and Rhodesians are vilified by other Africans, not because of differences in race, although this is the ostensible reason, but because these Africans whose parents came from Europe have been willing to do the work necessary for nation building. Relatively little of this nation building was done, or is being done now, in white shirts.

The black Africans of South Africa have higher living standards than that of any black African country. There are nearly thirteen million of them and they own more automobiles than Russia's total population of 220 million. Africans from all nations bordering on South Africa, as well as from other black-ruled nations, flock to South African mines to work at the highest wages available to them.

Zealous new African nations have yet to learn that other nations have made the mistakes they are making now and have never found all the answers in themselves. The trite accusation of "western" exploitation, colonialism, and interference has never applied in Africa's oldest kingdom of Ethiopia, nor has it for Liberia since the late 1800's, nor for the New World's Haiti since 1814, yet none of these countries have had the living standards of neighboring countries developed by outsiders.

Most newly independent African nations have discovered that the European influence they were so anxious to shed has been replaced by far more repressive influences from native leaders and minority tribal groups. Non-Kikuyus in Kenya have little chance of getting government jobs of consequence. The Kikuyu tribe numbers less than a quarter of the population of this country whose leadership is the most respected of all new African nations.

This apparent incongruity of wildlife and politics dissolves in reality. Africa's wildlife, one of her richest, and almost unexploited, resources, is dependent upon the attitudes of Africa's new leaders. Most of them seem to be aware of the need for preserving this magnetic resource which draws growing tourist crowds from every country.

Hopefully each visit will encourage a little more understanding between one man and another man. The average African and average American so far have had too few opportunities to meet each other and sit down for a talk.

Bibliography

Adamson, G. A. G. "Observation on Lions in Serengeti National Park, Tanganyika," *East African Wildlife Journal,* Volume 2, August, 1964.

Adamson, Joy. *Born Free.* Panthcon Books, 1960.

Forever Free. Harcourt, Brace & World, Inc., 1963.

Living Free. Harcourt, Brace & World, Inc., 1962.

Africana Magazine editors. "On the Edge of Danger," *Africana* Magazine, June, 1967.

Beebe, B. F. and Johnson, James Ralph. *American Bears.* David McKay Company, 1965.

Beirs, Margaret. *The Insects of Southern Africa.* Thomas Nelson and Sons (Africa) (PTY) Ltd., Johannesburg, 1964.

Cade, Robert. "Cheetah Just Tolerate Humans," *Africana* Magazine, June 1965.

Caras, Roger A. *Dangerous to Man.* Chilton Books, 1964.

Carr, Norman. *Return to the Wild.* E. P. Dutton & Company, Inc., 1962.

Daniel, Thase. "Tips of Africa," *Africana* Magazine, March, 1966.

Dominis, John. "The Cheetah," *Africana* Magazine, September, 1967.

"The Lion," *Africana* Magazine, December, 1967.

Downey, Syd. "Nonchalant Buffalo," *Africana* Magazine, September, 1965.

Durrell, Gerald M. *The Bafut Beagles.* Ballantine Books, Inc., 1963.

The Overloaded Ark. Ballantine Books, Inc., 1962.

A Zoo in My Luggage. Berkley Publishing Corporation, 1964.

Estes, Richard D. "Predators and Scavengers," *Natural History* Magazine, February and March, 1967.

Fosbrooke, H. A. "The Stomolys Plague in Ngorongoro, 1962," *East African Wildlife Journal,* Volume 1, August, 1963.

Gardner, Brian. *On To Kilimanjaro.* Macrae Smith Company, 1963.

Gee, E. P. *The Wildlife of India.* E. P. Dutton & Company, 1964.

Gill, Leonard. *South African Birds.* Maskew Miller, Ltd., Cape Town, 1964.

Goldthorpe, J. E. and Wilson, F. B. *Tribal Maps of East Africa and Zanzibar.* East African Institute of Social Research, Kampala, Uganda, 1960.

Graham, A. "East African Wild Life Society Cheetah Survey," *East African Wildlife Journal,* Volume 4, August, 1966.

Grizmek, Bernhard and Michael. *Serengeti Shall Not Die.* E. P. Dutton and Company, 1960.

Guggisberg, C. A. W. *Simba, the Life of the Lion.* Chilton Books, 1963.

Hallet, Jean-Pierre. *Congo Kitabu.* Fawcett World Library, 1967.

Hediger, Dr. H. *Wild Animals in Captivity.* Dover Publications, Inc., 1964.

Hunter, J. A. *Hunter.* Harper & Brothers, Publishers, 1952.

Kearney, Dennis. "Eland Wounds Lion," *Africana* Magazine, March, 1966.

Kenya Game Department. "Marking a Leopard," *East African Wildlife Journal,* Volume 3, August, 1965.

Kingsley-Heath, John. "The Man-Eater of Darajani," *Outdoor Life* Magazine, December, 1965.

Lake, Alexander. *Killers in Africa.* Doubleday & Company, Inc., 1953.

Maberly, C. T. Astley. *Animals of East Africa.* D. A. Hawkins, Ltd., Nairobi, 1965.
The Game Animals of Southern Africa. Thomas Nelson and Sons (South Africa) (Pty) Ltd., Johannesburg, 1963.

Murray, M., Campbell, Mrs. H. and Jarrett, W. H. F. "*Spirocerca lupi* in a Cheetah," *East African Wildlife Journal,* Volume 2, August, 1964.

O'Connor, Jack. "The Leopard," *Outdoor Life* Magazine, August, 1964.

Rikhoff, J. C. "Full House on Leopards," *Outdoor Life* Magazine, October, 1965.

Roosevelt, Kermit. "Leopard in Large Type," *Outdoor Life* Magazine, April, 1964.

Sanderson, Ivan T. *Animal Treasure.* The Viking Press, 1937.

Sanderson, Ivan and Loth, David. *Ivan Sanderson's Book of Great Jungles.* Simon and Schuster, 1965.

Stanek, V. J. *Pictorial Encyclopedia of the Animal Kingdom.* Crown Publishers, Inc., 1962.

Stokoe, W. J. *British Wild Animals.* Frederick Warne & Company, Ltd., London, 1953.

Sweeney, Charles. *The Scurrying Bush.* Chatto & Windus, London, 1966.

Tarlton, Alan. "One Man's Lions," *Africana* Magazine, September, 1964.

Turnbull-Kemp, Peter. *The Leopard.* Howard Timmins, Cape Town, 1967.

Turner, Myles. "Serengeti," *Africana* Magazine, September, 1965.

Tyrrell, P. R. "An Arabian Leopard," *East African Wildlife Journal,* Volume 1, August, 1963.

"U. S. and South Africa: The Ties, The Differences," *U. S. News & World Report*, April 22, 1968.

Varaday, Desmond. *Gara-Yaka, The Story of a Cheetah.* E. P. Dutton & Company, Inc., 1964.

Gara-Yaka's Domain. Collins, London, 1966.

Wender, Leo. *Animal Encyclopedia.* George Allen and Unwin, Ltd., London, 1966.

Williams, John G. *A Field Guide to the Birds of East and Central Africa.* Houghton Mifflin Company, 1964.

Shell Guide to East African Birds. Shell Oil Company, Nairobi, 1965.

Willock, Colin. *The Enormous Zoo.* Harcourt, Brace & World, 1965.

Woodman, Jim. *Air Travel Bargains Worldwide Guide-Book.* Pocket Books, Inc., 1967.

Yellowstone National Park Bear Incidents, 1931–1963. Yellowstone National Park, 1964.

Index

177